To Brian   20th Jan 1

from

Alan & Caroline.

D1587620

Brian,
          'now that you have left B5.5750 and
NTL behind, you will have plenty of time to
learn how to drive.
                    Best Wishes for the future.
I hope that the book will reduce you demand
on the photo copier et Sandy.

Alan & Caroline.

Filter Handbook

FILTER HANDBOOK

A practical design guide

Stefan Niewiadomski

Heinemann Newnes

To my wife, Anne, and children, Rebecca and Philip

Heinemann Newnes
An imprint of Heinemann Professional Publishing Ltd
Halley Court, Jordan Hill, Oxford OX2 8EJ

OXFORD LONDON MELBOURNE AUCKLAND
SINGAPORE IBADAN NAIROBI GABORONE
KINGSTON

First published 1989

British Library Cataloguing in Publication Data
Niewiadomski, Stefan
  Filter handbook.
  1. Electric filters. Design
  I. Title
  621.3815′324

ISBN 0 434 91378 2

Typeset by August Filmsetting, Haydock, St Helens
Printed and bound in Great Britain by
Courier International Ltd, Tiptree, Essex

Contents

Notes for US readers

The Filter Handbook has been written with a general audience in mind and not just for UK readers. However, in parts the book refers to standards and products which are more understandable and available to UK readers. This addendum explains these points and offers alternative sources for some of the components referred to in the text.

Toko is referred to extensively as a supplier of inductors. This company is now one of the very few sources of audio and RF coils at reasonable prices in the UK. The US address of Toko is: Toko America Inc., 1250 Feehanville Drive, Mt Prospect, Illinois 60056 (312–297–0070). Other possible sources of inductors in the US are Dale and Miller.

The sources given for low cost circuit simulators are all in the UK. Number One Systems will be pleased to accept enquiries from the US. In the US a catalogue of electronics software, including circuit analysis programs, is available from BV Engineering, 2200 Business Way, Suite 207, Riverside, Califoria 92501 (714–781–0252). An alternative supplier is Etron RF Enterprises, PO Box 4042, Diamond Bar, California 91765.

The BASIC prorams given in Chapter 7 are written using only low-level statements avoiding the graphical presentation of results which tends to make programs more machine dependent. This should make their translation for use on other BASIC machines, such as Apple, IBM PC, Commodore and so on, straightforward.

Where reference to the E12 range of resistors, capacitors and inductors is made, this refers to components having values which are power-of-ten multiples of 1.0, 1.2, 1.5, 1.8, 2.2, 2.7, 3.3, 3.9, 4.7, 5.6, 6.8 and 8.2. In the US, this range is generally referred to as 'the 10% tolerance range', which can be misleading since components with these values can be obtained with tighter tolerances than 10%

An alternative to the Siemens range of metallized polyester capacitors are Panasonic capacitors, available from Digi-Key Corporation, PO Box 677, Thief River Falls, Minnesota 56701 (1–800–344–4539).

1 Introduction

A filter, or more exactly an electric wave filter, is an electrical network which has some of its transfer characteristics frequency-dependent. The best known frequency-dependent characteristic of a filter is the input-to-output amplitude response, but other characteristics, such as the input-to-output phase relationship or the input impedance, can also vary with frequency.

The subject of filters, involving both the production of new designs and the examination of existing circuits suspected of being filters, has struck fear into the hearts of amateurs and professionals alike ever since their conception. For many years specialist knowledge and advanced mathematical skills were needed to obtain sufficient understanding of filter operation to be able to undertake design. The advent of modern filter design techniques in the 1950s, involving the use of pre-calculated lists of normalized component values for standard designs, did much to simplify filter design, helping to make the process possible for non-specialists. A more recent development has been the cheap availablity of calculators and home computers, which have put at the disposal of designers calculating power which fifteen years ago was solely available to professionals. Not only can this calculating power now be used to aid the design of filters, it can also be used to analyse any circuit, whether it is a filter or not, to determine its performance before buying the components and building it.

The importance of filters in electronics can be illustrated by looking at any piece of modern radio equipment. As an example, Fig. 1.1 is a simplified block diagram of the Lowe HF125 h.f. receiver which shows the considerable number of filters incorporated[1]. These include the passive low-pass, high-pass and band-pass filters in the front-end of the receiver; the band-pass crystal and ceramic filters in the I.F. stages (a passive low-pass filter is also selectable in the I.F. sages); the active low-pass P.L.L. filter; a 400Hz-wide active band-pass audio filter; and the tone-control network. A detailed examination of the circuit diagram reveals even more filters, mainly passive low-pass networks decoupling individual stages to reduce the possibility of interference between stages. No piece of modern radio gear could function without filters.

Aims of this book

The prime aim of this book is to describe the design process as applied to filters. The main emphasis will be on modern filter design, not only using tables of standard designs but also describing some more novel methods

1

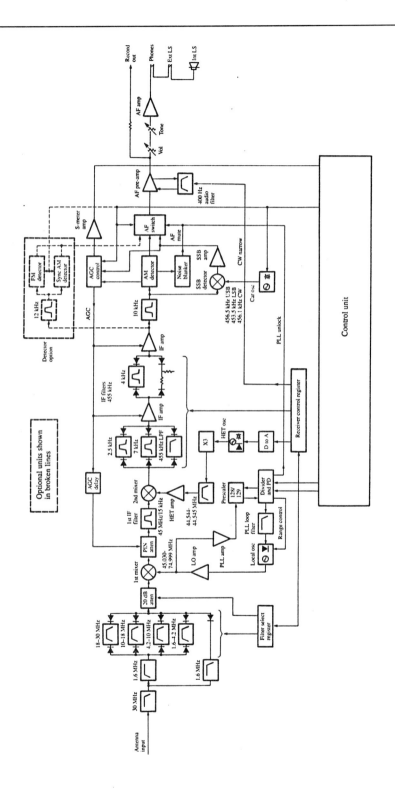

Figure 1.1 *Lowe HF-125 block diagram*

which calculators and home computers have made available to the amateur. Designers can therefore choose the method which suits them best. Computer-aided analysis which has much wider applications outside filters is also described, and some of the practical effects of approximation which, as a formal subject, is called sensitivity, are tackled. By using this book designers will be able to produce filters for many different applications, and also be able to predict the performance of existing designs.

Many people perceive filter design and analysis as being highly mathematical subjects. This does not have to be the case when using modern techniques and advanced mathematics will be largely avoided in this book. The use of graphs, tables, nomographs, calculators and home computers can hide the underlying mathematical nature of the subject and these aids will be used extensively here. Where more advanced mathematics is included to obtain a deeper understanding of a particular aspect for those who wish to, it can be completely ignored without detracting from the understanding of subsequent material.

People tend to have two basic ways of using a book. It can be read from cover to cover, following the flow chosen by the author to build up understanding of the subject. Alternatively, it can be used as a reference work, relevant sections being consulted as and when required. This book can be used in either way and whichever way is chosen it will help to dispel much of the mystique associated with filters.

Who is it aimed at?

The book is intended for three types of reader: firstly, those who have little or no experience of filters but who want to learn about the subject from scratch. This has been somewhat of a problem in the past: many books on electronics and radio contain brief sections about filters but they cannot go into much detail in the limited space available. Books which do consider the subject in depth usually contain too much mathematics for the average designer. It is also difficult to obtain these books: they can be expensive and are not usually found on the shelves of public libraries.

It is aimed secondly at those who have some knowledge of filters, may have already designed several and want to learn more or view the subject from a different standpoint. These people will probably have used the tables associated with the modern design technique, and the information given here will allow a more versatile approach for future designs, unfettered by the restrictions of the tabular method.

Thirdly, it is aimed at those who want to make use of their computers to design filters or to analyse circuits in general. Considerable scope for innovation and experimentation exists in the use of computers for filter design. The programs given here are presented as methods of carrying out particular steps in the design process. Keen programmers can work towards a completely integrated package, achieving the whole design process in a single program, possibly including computer graphics to make the best use of the capabilities of individual computers.

Inductors

Something must be said at this early stage about inductors. For many, filters are synonymous with inductors and inductors mean trouble, particularly ones with relatively high inductance values for use in audio filters. This is undoubtedly a major reason for the rapid introduction and development of active filters, once integrated-circuit operational amplifiers made them easy and cheap to implement. It is true that inductors have gained a bad reputation, especially amongst amateurs; after all, designers are not now usually expected to make their own resistors, capacitors, transistors and so on, and should not have to make their own inductors. Many types of wound inductors are now available, mainly originating in Japan and suitable for use at frequencies from audio to VHF. Wherever possible in this book when an inductor is required, as well as giving the exact inductance value an off-the-shelf component will be specified to allow the constructor to choose between either winding the inductor himself or buying the component. Constructors should therefore have no fear that inductors which are almost impossible to wind are going to be called for.

The design process

Before describing the contents of each chapter of the book it is interesting to examine the process of design with particular reference to filters.

A flowchart representing the steps involved in filter design is shown in

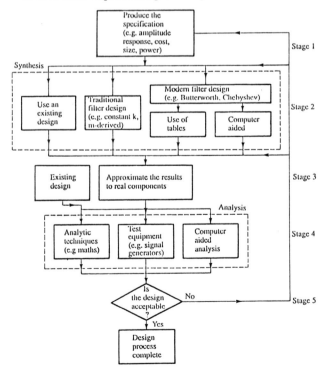

Figure 1.2 *The filter design technique*

Fig. 1.2. This sequence of events is typical of what happens during much of engineering design. The process can be divided into five basic stages: generating a specification; synthesizing a design; approximating the design to take account of real components; analysing the approximated design; and making a judgement as to whether the approximated design is acceptable. Each of these steps will now be looked at in detail.

Generating the specification

The first stage involves the formulation of a specification for the filter to be designed. Typically, this would involve the definition of the filter type (low-pass, high-pass, band-pass or band-stop), the allowable passband ripple, cut-off frequencies, driving and terminating impedances and so on. Also included might be some estimation of the preferred way to implement the design; experience might suggest that an active configuration will give the best solution. Limitations on the size and cost of the design might be relevant: a designer might want to include a detail such as the need to use 22 nF capacitors because they are available cheaply. How detailed and formal the specification is at this stage depends firstly on how well the problem to be solved is itself specified and secondly on the skill of the specifier. An experienced designer will be able to assess the importance of each parameter at this early stage and may be able to trade them off against each other with a feel for the final design.

A professional designer is likely to specify a tolerance for each parameter, but it is usual for the amateur to work with nominal values. What should be borne in mind is that, as the design process proceeds inaccuracies will occur and judgement will be required as to whether the performance has drifted too far from the original specification to be acceptable.

Synthesis

The second stage of the design process is the synthesis of the ideal solution which meets the specification produced earlier; three techniques are available at this stage. Firstly, an existing design might be available which meets the specification exactly or nearly so. Contrary to what some might feel, this is an entirely valid approach and if a suitable existing design can be found, this will lead to the quickest solution.

A second technique is the traditional method involving the design of L-sections of capacitors and inductors which can be combined into T and pi networks and then cascaded to form the complete filter. Design of these image-parameter constant-k and m-derived filters[2,3,4] requires the manipulation of many equations as low-pass and high-pass filters are built up section by section – a process which becomes even more tedious when band-pass responses are required. These filter families used to be found in the output stages of transmitters, but are seldom used today, and little more will be said about them here.

The third technique available at the synthesis stage is modern filter design, based upon Bessel, Butterworth and Chebyshev mathematical functions.

Using this technique, filters can be designed which perform better and possibly use less components than with the traditional methods. Figure 1.2 shows two approaches to design within this category: the use of pre-calculated tables or catalogues of standard designs, which is the usual approach; and a more versatile method using a computer, where the equations used to generate the tables are contained within a computer program or are solved using a calculator. This method allows infinite variation in the filter specification, since it is not restricted by the need to tabulate results in whatever limited number of pages the publisher has made available to the author. With this method, the specification is entered via a keyboard and the resulting design values are presented on a screen or printer.

Approximation

There now follows an essential part of the design process which may initally seem difficult but which, as a designer gains experience and confidence, becomes much easier. This is where the component values produced by the synthesis procedure, which have been calculated to an accuracy of perhaps four or more decimal places in the modern design method using tables or even twelve decimal places using the home computer, must be approximated to realistic values. These may simply be the E12 or E24 standard values, or serial or parallel combinations if greater accuracy is needed.

Another approximation which might be necessary is to take into account the properties of real components, rather than the idealized inductances, capacitances, op-amp characteristics and so on assumed during the synthesis process.

During this stage dramatic impacts can be made on the cost and ease of implementation of a design. For example, if it is decided that 1% capacitors must be used rather than 10%, their cost will be many times the more loosely toleranced components and they will be much more difficult to obtain. Similarly, if say a 197.1 mH inductor is called for, and the designer insists on this value being accurately adhered to, the cost of the wire and core assembly, the inconvenience of winding several hundred turns and the problem of accurately measuring the value could make the design unacceptable. However, if the designer knows that a 180 mH ready-wound inductor is available fairly cheaply, and that it will be acceptable in that application, then the design is made much more attractive.

Analysis

The next step involved is an analysis of the approximated design to assess how well it meets the original specification.

Three techniques are available at the analysis stage. Firstly, the design might be simple enough for analysis using mathematical formulae. A design does not have to involve many components before it becomes mathematically unmanageable, especially if effects such as the finite Q of inductors are taken into account.

The second technique is to build the design and measure its performance using test equipment such as a signal generator, oscilloscope and spectrum analyser. Of course, to test a filter accurately and thoroughly requires complex and expensive equipment, which is not available to many filter designers. By this point, the components for the design have been bought and, if the design proves to be a disaster because of a minor error somewhere in the synthesis stage, this can be an expensive way of discovering the error.

The third method available for analysis is the use of a computer running a circuit-analysis program, which takes most of the hard work out of the analysis stage; this is a powerful tool which has only recently become commonly available. One of the great advantages of this technique is that the performance of the ideal synthesized design can be compared with that of the approximated design, and so the effects of the approximation can be seen. Consider, for example, the effects of approximating and inductance into a real inductor: not only will the inductance value be altered, but capacitance and resistance will be added. The effect that each of these alterations to the ideal component has on the circuit operation can be investigated independently and the dominant ones identified. If required, several different approximations can be investigated until the best overall compromise between performance, cost and ease of construction is found.

At this stage simulation of the tentative design can also include the relevant parts of the driving and terminating circuits, so that the quality of the match they present to the filter can be seen.

The analysis stage can be used to examine existing designs which the designer might come across, either out of curiosity or as a potential solution to a problem. For this application, the computer-aided technique is clearly the most convenient, allowing a large number of designs to be investigated without having to buy any components.

Judgement

It is very unlikely that the results from the analysis process will exactly meet the original specification and so a judgement now has to be made to see whether they are close enough. If they are, then the stage has been reached where a final design has been obtained. If they are not acceptable, then some or all of the previous steps will have to be repeated. The number of steps to be repeated depends on how greatly the design deviates from the specification.

An important question must be asked: 'is the design reasonable for the intended application?' Although the performance might meet the specification, the implementation might use too many components, not fit into the available space, consume too much power or be too expensive for that particular application. An experienced designer should have anticipated these possibilities at the specification or approximation stages and made the correct decisions to avoid them.

Several iterations of one or more of the design stages may be necessary before the results are judged to be acceptable. The design process is finished only when the point is reached where the design meets the specification closely enough and the implementation is reasonable.

"Is the design reasonable?"

Summary

The design process consists of several discrete steps, some of which an experienced designer does almost subconsciously. These steps may have to be repeated, perhaps several times, before an acceptable solution for that particular application is found. Although the process has been described in terms of filter design, the steps involved are equally valid when designing other electrical circuits. In more general terms it can be applied to design in many fields, for example, in the design of a relatively simple mechanical component such as a small bracket, or a much more complex device such as an aircraft.

Modern filter design: the low-pass filter

Chapter 2 describes the basics of low-pass filter design using modern design techniques. The concept of normalization, which enables filter designs for any frequency and impedance level to be tabulated concisely, is explained. The ideal low-pass filter amplitude response is shown to be the solution to an unreasonable filtering specification and some tolerance must be added to a specification to allow a solution to be achieved. Simple low-pass filters, using only a few components, find widespread use in audio and radio frequency decoupling applications. Four named approximations to the ideal low-pass filter, namely Butterworth, Chebyshev, elliptic and Bessel, are described and the design of passive implementations of these filters shown using tables of pre-calculated component values. These approximations are the most useful to designers and will fulfil most filtering requirements. References are given to more extensive catalogues than the ones presented in this chapter.

High-pass, band-pass and band-stop filters

Chapter 3 is concerned with the important concept of transformation, whereby most high-pass, band-pass and band-stop filtering requirements can be traced back to a low-pass specification, a low-pass filter chosen which most closely meets this specification and a transformation applied to the low-pass prototype to make it meet the original requirement. The exception to this technique is when an asymmetrical filtering requirement must be met and the general solution to this type of requirement is to use cascaded or parallel-connected low-pass and high-pass filters.

Active low-pass filters

Chapter 4 deals with the design of active low-pass filters using op-amps. The design technique is similar to the passive case and again involves the use of catalogues of designs and component scaling to achieve the final circuit. Active filter design is seen as an extension of the passive filter design techniques described earlier and many of the concepts, such as filter approximation, normalization and scaling, are still valid. One advantage active filters have over passive filters is that they can easily be made tunable; that is, controls can be added to vary the cut-off frequency – a very useful facility in difficult communication situations where only the minimum bandwidth for intelligible communication is required. A relatively recent development in the control of the response of active filters involves the switching of capacitors and resistors at high frequency, varying the effective values of these components.

Active high-pass, band-pass and band-stop filters

Chapter 5 shows that active low-pass filters have high-pass equivalents, obtainable by similar transformation to that described in the passive case. Symmetrical band-pass and band-stop filters are best implemented using specifically designed sections, rather than with transformed low-pass sections. Band-pass and band-stop sections, which can be made tunable, can easily be designed and have numerous applications for peaking and rejecting narrow bands of frequencies. Once again, the best way to implement asymmetrical responses is by cascading or paralleling low-pass and high-pass filters. The advantage of using active filters in such applications is that the lower and upper cut-off frequencies can be made independently variable. Active and passive circuits can be mixed in the same filter, the well-defined low output impedance of the op-amp in an active section providing a convenient driving point for a passive filter.

Using real components

Chapter 6 tackles the problems facing the constructor. Filters are generally thought of as being more sensitive to component tolerances than other electronic circuits, but this is not necessarily true, particularly if the detrimental effects of the other parts of the system into which the filter fits are taken into account. A major cause of deterioration of passive filter responses, particularly at audio frequencies, is seen to be due to the use of inductors. But even so, very useful and inexpensive passive audio filters can be constructed using ready-wound inductors, which can only be matched in performance by very complex active filters. Practical filter designs for both audio and radio frequencies are presented and methods of incorporating these designs into the total system, while preserving good impedance matches to the filters, are explained.

Filter design software

Chapter 7 presents several BASIC programs, written for the Sinclair Spectrum computer, to help with the steps in the filter design process. As well as containing routines which perform relatively tedious, but important tasks (such as component scaling), programs are shown which allow new filters, not presented in the catalogues of Chapters 2 and 4, to be designed. Although the programs are written in Spectrum BASIC, statements have been avoided which would make implementation on another machine or in a different language difficult. Throughout this book, emphasis is placed on the importance of circuit simulation as a way of verifying the performance of a circuit before building it, avoiding the possibility of costly and time-consuming errors. Rather than write a simulation package, whose listing would not be publishable in this book because of its length, the author has concentrated on reviewing an inexpensive simulator which is available for several computers. Some other sources of such programs are also given and, no doubt, there are many more.

References

1. Lowe Electronics Ltd. HF125 receiver manual.
2. G.R. Jessop. (1985). *Radio Data Reference Book*, 5th edn. London: RSGB. p. 79.
3. W.I. Orr, W6SAI (1978). *Radio Handbook*, 21st edn. Sams pp. 3.28–3.30.
4. *Radio Communication Handbook*, 5th Edn. (1982). RSGB. p. 23.10.

2 Modern filter design: the low-pass filter

Although most designers are aware of the usefulness of the low-pass filter in itself, it is perhaps less well known that the modern approach to filter design relies on the selection of low-pass filters as prototypes in the design of all response types, including high-pass, band-pass and band-stop. Because low-pass filters form the basis of modern filter design, it is worthwhile spending some time looking firstly at the ideal low-pass filter response, at what approximations to the ideal are available and what they can achieve in comparison with the ideal.

In this chapter, passive implementations of the different filter types are shown, although many filters are now built incorporating active components, especially op-amps. The advantage of showing passive implementations at this early stage is that they generally use fewer components than their active counterparts and so it is easier to grasp the fundamental issues than if active implementations are shown. Passive filters are still used extensively, especially at radio frequencies where op-amps are no longer usable. Active filters will, of course, be dealt with in later chapters.

Those designers who are familiar with modern filter design will probably have used tables, or catalogues, of component values of standardized designs. The fact that this catalogue method has been so successful is evidence of the value of these catalogues and so several are included here. Even the cheapest of computers and scientific calculators now allow calculation of component values or the production of complete catalogues, and techniques for doing this are described.

Normalization

To offer tables of standard filter circuits, it is necessary to standardize some of the important parameters of the filters. The concept of normalization allows component values to be presented for filters with a cut-off frequency of 1 rad/s (0.1592 Hz)* and 1 Ω source and/or termination impedance. This frequency and impedance level leads to capacitor values in Farads and inductor values in Henries. These values of frequency and impedance, and the components themselves, may seem strange at first and it is the process of

---

* A radian is a circular measure of angle and equals approximately 57.3°. To convert from Hz to rad/s, multiply by 6.28.

scaling, which will be described later, which converts these normalized filters to work at useful frequencies and impedances.

Some catalogues may be enountered which are normalized to cut-off frequencies and impedances other than 1 rad/s, 1 Ω: 1 Hz cut-off frequency and 1 Ω impedance is one set of values sometimes used[1], and 1 MHz, 50 Ω is another[2]. In the author's opinion, normalization to any level other than 1 rad/s, 1 Ω is unnecessary and potentially misleading. Normalization to 1 Hz cut-off frequency simply saves the factor of 2 π when scaling – hardly significant when using a scientific calculator. An inexperienced designer coming across filter component values normalized to 1 MHz, 50 Ω could be excused for believing that they are intended for use only at radio frequencies, whereas such filters are equally valid for use in audio applications when correctly scaled.

The ideal low-pass filter response

Figure 2.1 shows the ideal low-pass filter amplitude response. In this diagram the vertical axis is labelled attenuation and increases downwards. Below the cut-off frequency, ω_c, inputs are passed with no attenuation, whereas above ω_c inputs are infinitely attenuated. Frequencies up to ω_c are termed the passband and above ω_c are the stopband. The transition from pass band to stopband is infinitely narrow. This response is unachievable in practice and represents the solution to an unreasonable filtering requirement. Consider, for example, what is required from a low-pass filter at the output of a transmitter to suppress harmonics of the output frequency which have been produced by non-linearities in the transmitter amplifier stages. The cut-off frequency of the filter will be set to the just greater than the highest operating frequency, to allow for some tolerance in the filter component values, and the filter will not have to attain a high attenuation value until twice the operating frequency. This simple view ignores the fact that other spurious frequency components between the fundamental and the first harmonic might be present at the transmitter output which the filter may have to attenuate, but it illustrates that there is usually no real requirement for an infinitely rapid transition from passband to stopband for a filter.

Figure 2.1 *The ideal low-pass filter amplitude response*

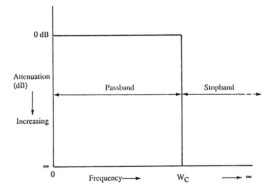

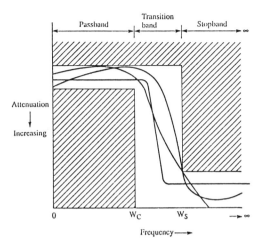

Figure 2.2 *One method of specifying a low-pass amplitude filtering requirement. The shading represents areas into which the response curve cannot enter. The specification can be met by an infinite number of responses, some of which are shown*

More realistic low-pass responses

A more reasonable way of specifying a low-pass filter is shown in Fig. 2.2. The unshaded area represents the freedom, or tolerance, that the designer has in which to place the response. The first freedom is that the passband does not have to be perfectly flat; so long as any variations, or ripples, in the responses remain within the unshaded area, the filter will meet the specification. Between the end of the passband and the beginning of the stopband a new region, the transition band, now exists which allows a reasonable frequency span for the attentuation to rise to the required stopband level. The stopband specification also has more freedom now than in the ideal response; the attentuation is only constrained not to fall below some minimum figure and, if it helps the design of the filter, it can have ripples similar to the passband.

An infinite number of responses can be fitted into the allowed area but some of these solutions, or approximations to the ideal low-pass response, are so useful that they have been thoroughly investigated and characterized over the years. Each approximation attempts to reproduce certain desirable characteristics of the ideal response, usually to the detriment of others. Many of these approximations (not to be confused with the approximation step described as part of the design process) have acquired the names of the men who did early work on them, or whose mathematical functions are used to describe their responses. Before looking in detail at some of these named approximations, some useful simple filters which are often found in radio circuits will be investigated. These will form a gentle introduction to the subject before more complicated responses are tackled.

Simple low-pass filters

Many problems can be solved by very simple low-pass-type responses implemented using only a few components. Consider the simple circuit shown in Fig. 2.3. The first question to ask is: 'Is it a filter and, if so, what type?' It is

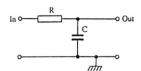

Figure 2.3 *A simple low-pass filter consisting of an RC network*

certainly a filter, since it contains one component, the capacitor, whose react-ance varies with frequency and so causes the output voltage to change as the input frequency is varied. It is a low-pass filter, since the reactance of the capacitor, given by $X_c = 1/\omega C$ where ω is the angular frequency in rad/s, decreases as frequency increases, causing a greater potential divider action in association with the resistor.

The cut-off frequency ω_c can be defined by $\omega_c = 1/RC$, where ω_c is in rad/s, R, is in ohms and C is in Farads. Note that in this simple example the cut-off frequency is only definable if R is known. The idealised amplitude response for this simple low-pass filter is shown in Fig. 2.4. In the example plotted, the value of R has been chosen to be 1 KΩ and C is 0.1592 μF, giving a cut-off frequency of 1 kHz. Beyond about 2 kHz, the response is tending towards a straight line (as viewed on a graph with both axes having logarithmic scales) of 6 dB/octave or 20 dB/decade. This configuration is said to have a single pole, or to have a first-order response, because there is one component, the capacitor, on which filter operation depends, whose reactance is tending towards some limiting value (in this case zero) at infinite frequency. This response is idealised in that it assumes that the capacitor value remains constant as frequency varies. In reality, not only will the capacitance change but its resistance and inductance will complicate the response obtained at higher frequencies.

This simple circuit is probably the most commonly used filter in electron-ics. It finds widespread application in decoupling, or preventing AC interfer-ence generated on supply rails by one block of circuitry from affecting another block. The circuit is often seen without the resistor, and its operation then depends on the rather vague properties of the driving voltage source, which will be some undefinable frequency-dependent combination of resistance, inductance, capacitance and pure voltage source. The resistor makes the performance much more predictable and should be included

Figure 2.4 *Amplitude response of the simple low-pass filter of fig 2.3 with R = 1KΩ, C = 0.1592 μF, giving a cut off (-3.01 dB) frequency of 1 KHz. In the stop-band the roll-off tends to 6 dB/octave or 20 dB/decade*

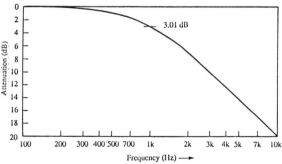

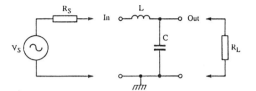

Figure 2.5 *A simple low-pass filter consisting of an LC network*

wherever possible, taking care to choose a value that does not cause excessive direct voltage drop due to the current flowing through it.

In some applications a parallel combination of a high-value electrolytic or tantalum capacitor and a smaller-value ceramic plate capacitor is used instead of the single capacitor. This gives good suppression over a wide band of frequencies, the high-value capacitor being effective for audio-frequency noise and the ceramic capacitor suppressing radio-frequency noise when the high-value capacitor has ceased to be effective as a capacitor. This configuration is still a first-order system, since inputs 'see' only a single capacitance, the parallel combination, which because of the practical limitations of capacitors varies with frequency.

In more critical applications the single-pole circuit may be inadequate. A second pole can be added, in the form of a series inductor, as shown in Fig. 2.5. Two effects are now preventing AC from passing from the input to the output: the increasing reactance of the inductor (given by $X_1 = \omega L$) and the decreasing reactance of the capacitor with frequency. This is therefore, a two-pole, or second-order, circuit.

The response of this circuit is not as easy to predict, because the inductor and capacitor form a series-resonant circuit which can produce a peak in the output voltage at a frequency given by $\omega_r = (LC)^{-\frac{1}{2}}$ rad/s (or $f_r = 1/2\pi (LC)^{\frac{1}{2}}$ Hz) so long as the damping effect of the source and terminating resistors is not too great. This damping effect can be quantified by calculating the Q values of the series leg (the $R_s L$ combination) and the shunt leg (the $C R_L$ combination). Assuming perfect components:

$$Q_1 = \frac{X_L}{R_s} \tag{2.1}$$

and $\quad Q_2 = \frac{R_L}{X_c} \tag{2.2}$

The total Q of the circuit is given by:

$$Q_{tot} = \frac{Q_1 Q_2}{Q_1 + Q_2} \tag{2.3}$$

The effect that Q_{tot} has on the amplitude response of the circuit is shown in Fig. 2.6: greater values of Q_{tot} give a more peaked response at ω_r and a greater initial roll-off, though the ultimate roll-off of all Q_{tot} values is the same. The peak in the response is only seen for Q_{tot} values greater than about 0.5. If the reader cares to try a few combinations of ω, L, C, R_s and R_L it will

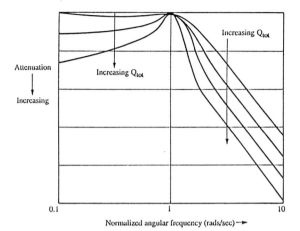

Figure 2.6 *Typical amplitude response of two pole LC Low-pass filters showing the effect of increasing Q_{tot}*

be seen to be difficult to arrive at the right combination to obtain a desired Q_{tot} value.

Again, this circuit is often seen decoupling power supply rails when the inductor is usually referred to as a choke, meaning that it can maintain a reasonable inductance value while passing the direct current needed by the circuit being fed. In this application, obtaining a peak in the response is not important and the exact values of R_s and R_L will be difficult, if not impossible, to predict. For most decoupling applications, a 1 mH choke and a high-quality $0.1\,\mu$F or 10 nF ceramic capacitor will give good decoupling action for radio frequencies, with the capacitor increased to say $100\,\mu$F for audio applications.

The Butterworth response

Figure 2.7 shows the typical amplitude response of a Butterworth low-pass filter. The Butterworth approximation is arrived at by insisting that the amplitude response is flat at zero frequency. This is why this response is often called maximally flat, which is sometimes misinterpreted as meaning that it

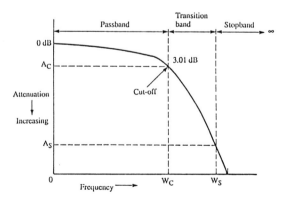

Figure 2.7 *The idealized Butterworth low-pass filter response. Cut-off is defined as the frequency at which the attenuation reaches 3.01 dB. The start of stop-band is arbitrarily defined by the designer as the frequency at which the attenuation reached A_s dB*

has the lowest attenuation throughout the passband of all filter types; in fact, the term maximally flat refers to its response at and just above zero frequency. As the order of the filter is increased the accuracy of the approximation to a flat passband improves.

The cut-off frequency for this type of filter is defined as the frequency at which the output power has fallen to half its zero-frequency level: that is the 3.01 dB voltage-attenuation point (commonly abbreviated to simply 3 dB). Note that nothing magical happens at the cut-off frequency: a common misconception is that it marks the frequency beyond which the filter offers infinite attenuation to inputs, which is untrue. The response beyond cut-off is said to be monotonic, that is the attenuation constantly increases (in theory at least) as frequency increases. There is no obvious characteristic which defines the end of the transition band and the start of the stopband. The designer of the filter must define this by specifying a frequency, ω_s, at which the attenuation must reach a certain value, A_s.

Filters produced using the Butterworth approximation turn out to be a compromise between steepness of attenuation beyond cut-off and initial flatness in the passband. In the context of circuit Q described in the previous section, Butterworth filters are considered to be of medium-Q.

The attenuation A of a Butterworth low-pass filter is given by:

$$A = 10 \log_{10}\left[1 + \left(\frac{\omega}{\omega_c} \right)^{2n} \right] dB \qquad (2.4)$$

where ω is the angular frequency in rad/s at which the attenuation is desired,
   ω_c is the cut-off angular frequency in rad/s,
   n is the order of the filter, which is equal to the number of elements in the filter in its passive implementation.

This equation can be used to find the attenuation at any frequency; below, at or above the cut-off frequency. It is a good example of how calculators and computers have simplified filter design; evaluating this equation using a slide-rule or logarithm tables would be laborious and prone to error, but nowadays presents no problems. By evaluating this equation at various frequen-

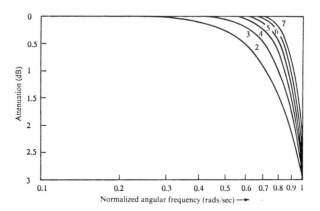

Figure 2.8 *Butterworth low-pass filters passband response for* $n = 2$ *to* 7

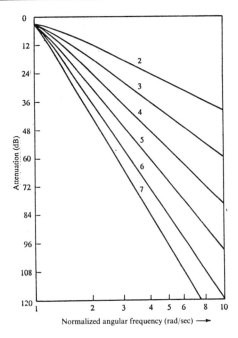

Figure 2.9 *Butterworth low-pass filters stopband response for n = 2 to 7*

cies for several of n, a family of curves can be generated which illustrate the attentuation achieved by filters of these orders at any frequency. Figures 2.8 and 2.9 show this information for frequencies below and above cut-off (normalized to 1 rad/s) respectively. Fig. 2.8 shows that, as the order of the filter increases, the responses remains flatter for more of the passband.

The ultimate roll-off rate of a Butterworth filter (beyond about twice the cut-off frequency) is $6n$ dB per octave, where n is the order of the filter. A sixth-order filter, therefore, can be expected to have about 36 dB more attenuation at four times the cut-off frequency than it had at twice the cut-off frequency, and another 36 dB attenuation at eight times the cut-off frequency.

Figure 2.9 provides a handy method of assessing the order of Butterworth filter needed to meet a given stopband attenuation specification. For example, say a filter is needed with an attenuation of 40 dB at twice the cut-off frequency. Figure 2.9 shows that a sixth-order Butterworth filter has only 36 dB attenuation at 2 rad/s, whereas a seventh-order filter has 42 dB attenuation at this frequency. Therefore the seventh-order filter is required. This is a good example of how discrepances occur when an attempt is made to implement a filtering specification. Even at this early stage of design, the rounding up of the filter order will cause the attenuation at 2 rad/s to be greater than originally specified 40 dB.

An alternative way of determining the order of a Butterworth filter is to use the equation:

$$n = \frac{\log_{10}[10^{A/10} - 1]}{2 \log_{10}\left(\dfrac{\omega}{\omega_c}\right)} \tag{2.5}$$

where the symbols have the same meanings as in equation 2.4.

Equation 2.5 is simply a rearrangement of equation 2.4. In general a non-integer answer for n will be obtained and, since a filter can only have an integral number of components, the answer must be rounded up. Using the 40 dB filter above as an example, the answer obtained for n using equation 2.5 is 6.644 which, when rounded up, gives 7 as deduced from Fig. 2.9.

So long as a filter having equal source and termination impedances is required, calculating component values is relatively simple. The component values for the passive implementation of a normalized Butterworth filter having 1 Ω source and terminating impedances is given by

$$\text{COMP}_k = 2 \sin\frac{(2k-1)\pi}{2n} \quad \text{for } k = 1, 2 \ldots n \tag{2.6}$$

where COMP_k is the k-th component, being either a shunt capacitor (in Farads) or a series inductor (in Henries), of the circuit in Fig. 2.10,

n is the order of the filter.

Be careful when evaluating this equation on a calculator to work in radians, not degrees. Using equation 2.6, component values for filter complexities of $n = 2$ to 7 have been calculated and are shown in Table 2.1. Com-

Table 2.1 *Butterworth low-pass LC element values*

FILTER	ORDER	C1	L2	C3	L4	C5	L6	C7
B02	2	1.4142	1.4142					
B03	3	1.0000	2.0000	1.0000				
B04	4	0.7654	1.8478	1.8478	0.7654			
B05	5	0.6180	1.6180	2.0000	1.6180	0.6180		
B06	6	0.5176	1.4142	1.9319	1.9319	1.4142	0.5176	
B07	7	0.4450	1.2470	1.8019	2.0000	1.8019	1.2470	0.4450
FILTER	ORDER	L1	C2	L3	C4	L5	C6	L7

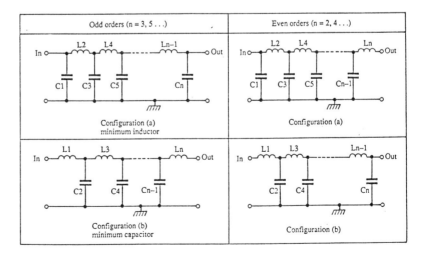

Figure 2.10 *Butterworth, Chebyshev and Bessel low-pass filter passive implementations*

ponent values for values of n greater than 7 can easily be calculated from equation 2.6 if required.

Note that two basic configurations are shown in Fig. 2.10: (a) has a shunt capacitor and (b) has a series inductor as the first element. These networks are duals of each other, meaning that they have identical responses in all respects. For even values of n ($n = 2,4\ldots$) there is little to choose between them, but when n is odd (a) has one fewer inductor than (b). Since inductors are usually more expensive and less easy to obtain than capacitors, configuration (a) is usually chosen when an equal-terminations, low-pass filter is needed. Configuration (b), however, offers advantages when unequal terminations are required, or when the low-pass filter is only a prototype to be transformed into a different response, as will be seen in Chapter 3.

A shorthand method of describing filters by a code has been devised which considerably simplifies reference to different filters. In the case of Butterworth filters only the order needs to be stated to describe fully the nature of its response. For Butterworth filters the form of the code is Bn. The initial letter of the word Butterworth is used to describe the type of response, followed by the order, n. A second-order Butterwoth filter can therefore be described as B02, a third-order as B03 and so on. Other filter types require more description.

Sometimes a filter is required to operate between unequal terminations. Rather than give tables of designs able to operate between unequal terminations here, reference should be made to Chapter 7, where the method of design is described, and a BASIC program which produces the component values for such filters is given. Alternatively, references 3, 4 and 5 tabulate normalized component values for Butterworth filters capable of working between unequal terminations.

The Chebyshev response

Whereas the Butterworth approximation results in an increasing deviation from the flat passband of the ideal low-pass filter as frequency increases, the Chebyshev approximation aims to distribute the deviation evenly across the

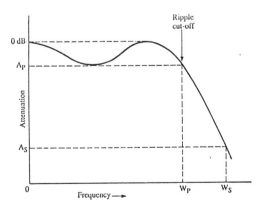

Figure 2.11 *The idealised Chebyshev low-pass filter response*

passband as ripples. Each ripple is of equal amplitude and the maximum ripple value is given the symbol A_p. Figure 2.11 shows the typical amplitude response of a third-order Chebyshev low-pass filter. It is seen to be a third-order response because there are three half cycles of passband ripple; a fifth-order filter would have five half cycles and so on. As with the Butterworth approximation, Chebyshev filters are monotonic in the stopband. A_s and ω_s are again chosen by the designer to specify the stopband performance of the filter. Chebyshev filters are considered to be of high Q, increasing as the amplitude of passband ripple is increased.

Different authors have different ways of defining the cut-off frequency of Chebyshev filters and the unwary can become confused. Some [references 6, 7, 8] define it in a similar way to the Butterworth response: that is, as the frequency at which the attenuation reaches 3 dB. Others [references 9, 10, 11] define it as the frequency at which the attenuation first exceeds the permitted passband ripple value. Confusion arises because, for a given passband ripple, two supposedly normalized filters having their cut-off frequencies defined in these two different ways will have different component values. If a catalogue of Chebyshev filters is encountered, simulation of one of the filters will reveal which definition of cut-off has been used if this is not stated. In this book the latter definition, that is the ripple cut-off point, will be used. To avoid confusion, the frequency at which it occurs will be referred to as ω_p, rather than ω_c.

No matter what amplitude of passband ripple is allowed, for a given order of filter, the peaks and troughs of the ripples occur at the same frequencies. These frequencies can easily be calculated from the formula

$$\omega_{rip} = \cos\frac{k\pi}{2n} \quad \text{for } k = 0,1,2\ldots n \tag{2.7}$$

where ω_{rip} is the angular frequency at which the peaks and troughs occur (normalized to 1 rad/s)
       n is the order of the filter.

The magnitude of passband ripple can be expressed in several ways: it can be as a relative amplitude in dB; as a ripple factor; as a voltage standing-wave ratio (VSWR), a term familiar to most engineers as a measure of how good a match a load presents to a device which is sensitive to mismatches; or as a reflection coefficient. Designers may come across any of these terms in filter literature and it is useful to be able to convert between them.

If the passband ripple is A_p dB, then the ripple factor, ε, is given by

$$\varepsilon = \sqrt{10^{A_p/10} - 1} \tag{2.8}$$

For values of A_p less than 3.01 dB, which is usually the case, ε works out to be less than 1.

The VSWR can be calculated from ε and is given by

$$\text{VSWR} = \frac{1+\varepsilon}{1-\varepsilon} \tag{2.9}$$

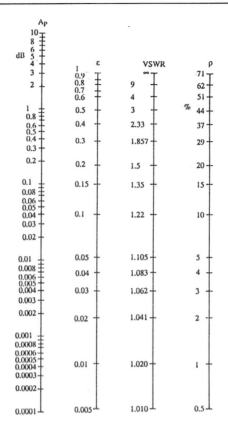

Figure 2.12 *Nomograph showing the relationship between attentuation (A_p), Ripple factor (ε), VSWR and Reflection Coefficient (ρ) as a percentage. To convert from one quantity to another, draw a horizontal line through the initial quantity and read where the line intersects the other scale.*

The reflection coefficient, ρ, can be calculated from A_p by the equation

$$\rho = \sqrt{1 - 10^{-A_p/10}} \qquad (2.10)$$

ρ is usually expressed as a percentage.

Figure 2.12 is a nomograph which can be used to convert between A_p, ε, VSWR and ρ. A nomograph allows the calculation of some quantity by constructing lines on a diagram, thereby reducing an algebraic process (solving an equation) to a geometric process (drawing lines). Many nomographs exist in electronics; there are ones for calculating series and parallel combinations of resistors, for example. The only potential drawback of nomographs is that they are generally less accurate than using the algebraic method. To use the nomograph of Fig. 2.12, simply draw a horizontal line through the known value of A_p, ε, VSWR or ρ and read from the other scales the corresponding values of the other quantities.

One beneficial property of the Chebyshev response is that it can have a faster initial roll-off beyond the cut-off frequency than a Butterworth filter of the same order. Plots of the responses beyond cut-off of 0.1 dB passband-ripple Chebyshev filters for $n = 2$ to 7 are shown in Fig. 2.13. Comparing Fig. 2.13 with Fig. 2.9 (the Butterworth stopband responses) shows that the

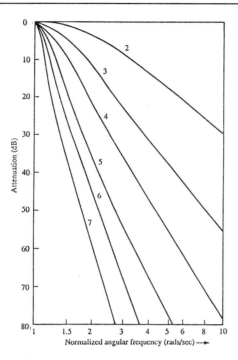

Figure 2.13 *Stopband response of 0.1 dB pass-band ripple Chebyshev low-pass filters for n = 2 to 7*

$n = 2$ and $n = 3$ Chebyshev filters have a slower roll-off rate than the same order Butterworth filters but, for $n = 4$ and above, the Chebyshev filters have a faster roll-off. For 1 dB passband-ripple Chebyshev filters, the $n = 2$ filter is marginally worse than the Butterworth equivalent up to about 4 rad/s and then becomes better at higher frequencies. Higher-order 1 dB passband-ripple Chebyshev filters are progressively better than the same order Butterworth filters.

As more passband ripple is allowed, the initial roll-off becomes even steeper. For example, for fifth-order Chebyshev filters, the 1 dB ripple filter has approximately 10 dB greater attenuation at twice the cut-off frequency than the 0.1 dB ripple filter, which itself has 10 dB more attenuation than the 0.01 dB ripple filter. Alternatively, this improvement in stopband performance can be expressed as the 1 dB ripple filter achieving an attenuation of say 50 dB at $\omega = 2.1$ rad/s rather than at 2.7 rad/s for the 0.1 dB filter, and 3.4 rad/s for the 0.01 dB ripple filter. The ultimate roll-off rate of Chebyshev filters, no matter what value of passband ripple is allowed, is identical to the Butterworth case, that is $6n$ dB per octave, where n is the order of the filter.

Because the passband ripple value has to be taken into account when assessing what order of Chebyshev filter is needed to satisfy a specification, another nomograph is shown in Fig. 2.4 for this purpose. The use of this nomograph is best illustrated by an example (see Fig. 2.15): say a Chebyshev filter is required with a maximum passband ripple of 1 dB and a minimum stopband attenuation of 40 dB at three times the cut-off frequency. A line is drawn from the 1 dB point on the A_p scale, through the 40 dB point on the A_s scale and extended until it meets the left-hand vertical axis of the area on

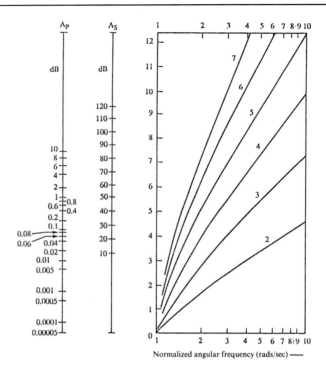

Figure 2.14 *Nomograph for Chebyshev filters*

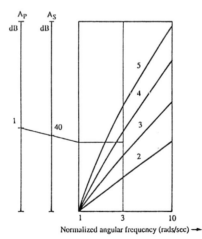

Figure 2.15 *Use of the nomograph of Fig. 2.14 to assess the order required of a Chebyshev low-pass filter with $A_p = 1\,dB$ and $A_s = 40\,dB$ at 3 rads/s*

which curves for different values of *n* are drawn. A line is then drawn horizontally until it meets the 3 rad/s vertical axis. In this example, this occurs somewhere between the $n = 3$ and $n = 4$ curves, indicating that a fourth-order filter must be used in practice. Because a greater order than theoretically required has to be used, the actual attenuation at 3 rad/s will be greater than 40 dB.

The attenuation of a Chebyshev filter at an angular frequency of ω rad/s can be calculated from the equation

$$A = 10 \log_{10} [1 + \varepsilon^2 (\cosh (n \cosh^{-1} \omega))^2] \, \text{dB} \tag{2.11}$$

where ε is the ripple factor,
n is the order of the filter.

Some calculators and simpler computers may not have hyperbolic functions available. In that case the following relationships will be useful: $\cosh x = (e^x + e^{-x})/2$ and $\cosh^{-1} x = \ln (x + \sqrt{x^2 - 1})$.

For the fourth-order 1 dB passband-ripple filter discussed above, equation 2.11 gives an attenuation of approximately 49.4 dB at 3 rad/s.

The calculation and tabulation of passive component values for Chebyshev filters is more involved than for the Butterworth response because a new degree of freedom, A_p, has been introduced. The most commonly used method is to refer to tables of normalized designs, and seven are shown in Tables 2.2–2.8. For the odd-order filters ($n = 3, 5 \ldots$) R_s and R_L are both normalized to 1 Ω, but even-order Chebyshev filters ($n = 2, 4 \ldots$) cannot operate correctly between equal terminations. In the tables, therefore, component values have been given for one ratio of R_L/R_s (or its inverse with the dual implementation) in the even-order case: the value of R_s is 1 Ω for both the odd and even-order implementations. The interpretation of the tables is exactly as for the Butterworth tables and the values again refer to the circuit configurations of Fig. 2.10.

Because of the limitations on space in this chapter, only one value of R_L/R_s (or R_s/R_L) is shown in Tables 2.2–2.8. There is an infinite number of impedance ratios between which Chebyshev filters of odd and even orders can be designed to operate. The method of designing these filters and a BASIC program which performs the calculations are given in Chapter 7. Alternatively, references 6, 7 and 8 contain tables of component values for Chebyshev filters suitable for use between unequal terminations.

For each of the filters in Tables 2.2–2.8, an identifying code is given. To identify a Chebyshev filter uniquely the order and the passband ripple need to be defined and the form of the code is Cnp. The capital C indicates the Chebyshev approximation and the passband ripple is defined in the reflection coefficient format as a percentage with any digits after the decimal truncated. A third-order 1 dB passband-ripple Chebyshev filter is therefore referred to as C03 45. Similarly, C05 24 is a fifth-order 0.25 dB passband-ripple Chebyshev filter. In some books, the letter T might be found denoting the Chebyshev response. This results from the initial letter of an alternative spelling of Chebyshev, namely Tchebycheff.

Table 2.2 *0.01 dB passband ripple Chebyshev LC element values*

FILTER	ORDER	R1/Rs	C1	L2	C3	L4	C5	L6	C7
C02 04	2	0.5	0.9920	0.1450					
C03 04	3	1.0	0.6292	0.9703	0.6292				
C04 04	4	0.5	2.0757	0.6313	2.0413	0.2152			
C05 04	5	1.0	0.7563	1.3049	1.5773	1.3049	0.7563		
C06 04	6	0.5	2.4582	0.7951	3.1418	0.7229	2.2328	0.2322	
C07 04	7	1.0	0.7969	1.3924	1.7481	1.6331	1.7481	1.3924	0.7969
FILTER	ORDER	Rs/R1	L1	C2	L3	C4	L5	C6	L7

Table 2.3 *0.025 dB passband ripple Chebyshev LC element values*

FILTER	ORDER	R1/Rs	C1	L2	C3	L4	C5	L6	C7
CO2 07	2	0.5	1.2129	0.1874					
CO3 07	3	1.0	0.7575	1.0592	0.7575				
CO4 07	4	0.5	2.2171	0.6917	2.2918	0.2587			
CO5 07	5	1.0	0.8803	1.3549	1.7091	1.3549	0.8803		
CO6 07	6	0.5	2.5294	0.8308	3.2797	0.7775	2.4670	0.2751	
CO7 07	7	1.0	0.9183	1.4283	1.8594	1.6352	1.8594	1.4283	0.9183
FILTER	ORDER	Rs/R1	L1	C2	L3	C4	L5	C6	L7

Table 2.3 0.025 dB passband ripple Chebyshev LC element values.

Table 2.4 *0.05 dB passband ripple Chebyshev LC element values*

FILTER	ORDER	R1/Rs	C1	L2	C3	L4	C5	L6	C7
CO2 10	2	0.5	1.3942	0.2302					
CO3 10	3	1.0	0.8794	1.1132	0.8794				
CO4 10	4	0.5	2.3041	0.7410	2.4845	0.3027			
CO5 10	5	1.0	0.9984	1.3745	1.8283	1.3745	0.9984		
CO6 10	6	0.5	2.5613	0.8601	3.3594	0.8228	2.6461	0.3187	
CO7 10	7	1.0	1.0346	1.4369	1.9637	1.6162	1.9637	1.4369	1.0346
FILTER	ORDER	Rs/R1	L1	C2	L3	C4	L5	C6	L7

Table 2.5 *0.1 dB passband ripple Chebyshev lowpass LC element values*

FILTER	ORDER	R1/Rs	C1	L2	C3	L4	C5	L6	C7
CO2 15	2	0.5	1.5715	0.2880					
CO3 15	3	1.0	1.0316	1.1474	1.0316				
CO4 15	4	0.5	2.2345	0.7973	2.6600	0.3626			
CO5 15	5	1.0	1.1468	1.3712	1.9750	1.3712	1.1468		
CO6 15	6	0.5	2.5561	0.8962	3.3962	0.8761	2.8071	0.3785	
CO7 15	7	1.0	1.1812	1.4228	2.0967	1.5734	2.0967	1.4228	1.1812
FILTER	ORDER	Rs/R1	L1	C2	L3	C4	L5	C6	L7

Table 2.6 *0.25 dB passband ripple Chebyshev LC element values*

FILTER	ORDER	R1/Rs	C1	L2	C3	L4	C5	L6	C7
CO2 24	2	0.5	1.7288	0.4104					
CO3 24	3	1.0	1.3034	1.1463	1.3034				
CO4 24	4	0.5	2.2884	0.9039	2.7832	0.4930			
CO5 24	5	1.0	1.4144	1.3180	2.2414	1.3180	1.4144		
CO6 24	6	0.5	2.4162	0.9771	3.2941	0.9837	2.9094	0.5100	
CO7 24	7	1.0	1.4468	1.3560	2.3476	1.4689	2.3476	1.3560	1.4468
FILTER	ORDER	Rs/R1	L1	C2	L3	C4	L5	C6	L7

Table 2.7 *0.5 dB passband ripple Chebyshev LC element values*

FILTER	ORDER	R1/Rs	C1	L2	C3	L4	C5	L6	C7
CO2 32	2	0.5	1.5132	0.6538					
CO3 32	3	1.0	1.5963	1.0967	1.5963				
CO4 32	4	0.5	1.8158	1.1328	2.4882	0.7732			
CO5 32	5	1.0	1.7058	1.2296	2.5408	1.2296	1.7058		
CO6 32	6	0.5	1.8786	1.1884	2.7589	1.2404	2.5976	0.7976	
CO7 32	7	1.0	1.7373	1.2582	2.6383	1.3443	2.6383	1.2582	1.7373
FILTER	ORDER	Rs/R1	L1	C2	L3	C4	L5	C6	L7

Table 2.7 0.5 dB passband ripple Chebyshev LC element values.

Table 2.8 *1 dB passband ripple Chebyshev LC element values*

FILTER	ORDER	R1/Rs	C1	L2	C3	L4	C5	L6	C7
CO2 45	2	0.25	3.7779	0.3001					
CO3 45	3	1.0	2.0236	0.9941	2.0236				
CO4 45	4	0.25	4.5699	0.5428	5.3680	0.3406			
CO5 45	5	1.0	2.1349	1.0911	3.0009	1.0911	2.1349		
CO6 45	6	0.25	4.7366	0.5716	6.0240	0.5764	5.5353	0.3486	
CO7 45	7	1.0	2.1666	1.1115	3.0936	1.1735	3.0936	1.1115	2.1666
FILTER	ORDER	Rs/R1	L1	C2	L3	C4	L5	C6	L7

The elliptic response

One feature of the ideal low-pass response which the Butterworth and Chebyshev approximations attempt to mimic is infinite attenuation in the stopband, though in practice this will be impossible to achieve due to leakage around the filter and the non-ideal nature of the components forming the filter. In many applications, it is only important that some attenuation is attained at a specified frequency and that this attenuation is at least maintained as frequency increases, without having to tend towards infinity. This stopband response is characteristic of the elliptic or Cauer approximation, which results in a high circuit Q for the filter.

Figure 2.16 shows the idealized amplitude response of an elliptic low-pass

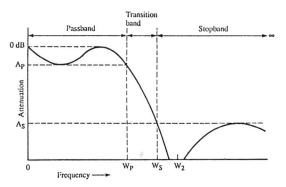

Figure 2.16 *The ideal elliptic low-pass filter response. This is the typical response of a third order filter, as shown in Fig.2.17*

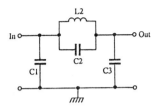

Figure 2.17 *Third order elliptic low-pass filter circuit diagram. The parallel tuned circuit formed by C2 and L2 gives the frequency of infinite attenuation, W_2, shown on Fig. 2.19*

filter. The passband response is similar to the Chebyshev case, having ripples and cutting off at ω_p, where the attenuation first exceeds the passband-ripple value, A_p. The transition band lies between ω_p and ω_s, where the attenuation first reaches A_s, the minimum value specified as being acceptable. At a frequency of ω_2 in the stopband the attenuation of the filter is infinite and beyond this frequency the attenuation decreases towards A_s, reaches A_s and then increases again. This response is typical of the three-branch elliptic filter shown in Fig. 2.17. The reason for the frequency of infinite attenuation can now be seen: L_2 and C_2 form a series-connected parallel tuned circuit and so, at a frequency $\omega_2 = 1/\sqrt{L_2.C_2}$, this tuned circuit ideally offers an infinite impedance to the input, resulting in no output. Designers familiar with radio circuits may have encountered series-connected parallel tuned circuits as traps, placed in a signal path to reject a specific frequency. In this application they are acting as band-stop filters, and this type of filter is described in the next chapter.

As with the Chebyshev response, the number of half ripples in the passband is equal to the order of the filter. If a fifth-order response is plotted, five half ripples are seen in the passband and there are two frequencies of high attenuation in the stopband, being the resonant frequencies of the pairs of capacitors and inductors which form the upper branches.

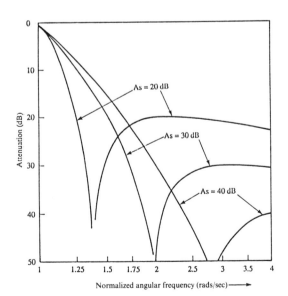

Figure 2.18 *Elliptic low-pass filter stopband responses for $A_s = 20$, 30 and 40 dBs $A_p = 1$ dB and $n = 3$ for all cases shown*

As the Chebyshev response introduced a new variable, the passband ripple, to the Butterworth response, the elliptic response introduces another variable, A_s. The value of A_s can be chosen at the specification stage and, in many applications, this is a more realistic way of defining a filtering requirement than the tending-towards-infinity response of other approximations. All other things being equal, the value of A_s and the roll-off rate beyond cut-off can be traded off against each other, as shown in Fig. 2.18. The three responses plotted are $n = 3$, $A_p = 1$ dB filters having A_s values of 20 dB, 30 dB and 40 dB. The 20 dB filter reaches its A_s value at 1.25 rad/s, the 30 dB filter at 1.7 rad/s and the 40 dB filter at 2.4 rad/s. Therefore, one way of increasing the roll-off rate of an elliptic filter is to reduce the value of A_s required.

Another way of increasing the roll-off rate is to increase the permitted passband ripple, A_p, exactly as with the Chebyshev response. Finally, as would be expected, the order of the filter can be increased to give a faster roll-off.

Selection of the order of elliptic filter required to meet a particular specification can be achieved using the nomograph of Fig. 2.19. Its use is identical to the one given for Chebyshev filters, remembering that A_s is now only the guaranteed minimum stopband attenuation, whereas for the Chebyshev filter it was the attenuation at the beginning of the stopband as defined by the designer and was guaranteed to increase, in theory at least, at higher frequencies.

Component values for the elliptic low-pass passive implementation are given in Tables 2.9–2.11 and the component designations refer to the circuits of Fig. 2.20. Values are shown for $n = 3$, 5 and 7 with four A_p magnitudes (0.011, 0.044, 0.177 and 1.249 dB) and twenty values of A_s for each combination of order and passband ripple. A considerable number of useful designs

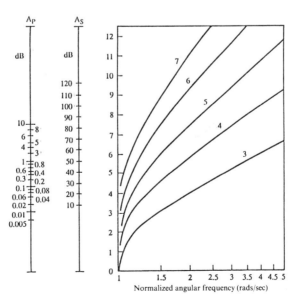

Figure 2.19 *Nomograph for elliptic filters*

Table 2.9 *Normalized component values for third order elliptic low-pass passive filters with passband ripples of 0.011, 0.044, 0.177 and 1.249 dB*

FILTER	Ap	As	ws	C1	C2	L2	C3
CC03 05 02	0.011	85.5	28.65	0.6390	0.0009	0.9776	0.6390
CC03 05 03	0.011	74.9	19.11	0.6381	0.0021	0.9761	0.6381
CC03 05 04	0.011	67.4	14.34	0.6370	0.0037	0.9739	0.6370
CC03 05 05	0.011	61.6	11.47	0.6354	0.0059	0.9711	0.6354
CC03 05 06	0.011	56.9	9.57	0.6336	0.0085	0.9676	0.6336
CC03 05 07	0.011	52.8	8.21	0.6314	0.0116	0.9636	0.6314
CC03 05 08	0.011	49.3	7.19	0.6289	0.0152	0.9589	0.6289
CC03 05 09	0.011	46.3	6.39	0.6261	0.0193	0.9536	0.6261
CC03 05 10	0.011	43.5	5.76	0.6229	0.0240	0.9477	0.6229
CC03 05 11	0.011	41.0	5.24	0.6194	0.0291	0.9411	0.6194
CC03 05 12	0.011	38.7	4.81	0.6155	0.0349	0.9339	0.6155
CC03 05 13	0.011	36.6	4.45	0.6113	0.0412	0.9261	0.6113
CC03 05 14	0.011	34.7	4.13	0.6068	0.0482	0.9177	0.6068
CC03 05 15	0.011	32.9	3.86	0.6020	0.0558	0.9087	0.6020
CC03 05 16	0.011	31.1	3.63	0.5968	0.0640	0.8991	0.5968
CC03 05 17	0.011	29.5	3.42	0.5913	0.0729	0.8888	0.5913
CC03 05 18	0.011	28.0	3.24	0.5855	0.0826	0.8780	0.5855
CC03 05 19	0.011	26.6	3.07	0.5793	0.0930	0.8665	0.5793
CC03 05 20	0.011	25.2	2.92	0.5728	0.1043	0.8545	0.5728
CC03 05 21	0.011	24.0	2.79	0.5661	0.1164	0.8418	0.5661
CC03 10 03	0.044	81.0	19.11	0.8521	0.0019	1.1015	0.8521
CC03 10 04	0.044	73.5	14.34	0.8510	0.0033	1.0997	0.8510
CC03 10 05	0.044	67.7	11.47	0.8496	0.0052	1.0973	0.8496
CC03 10 06	0.044	62.9	9.57	0.8479	0.0075	1.0944	0.8479
CC03 10 07	0.044	58.9	8.21	0.8459	0.0102	1.0910	0.8459
CC03 10 08	0.044	55.4	7.19	0.8436	0.0134	1.0871	0.8436
CC03 10 09	0.044	52.3	6.39	0.8410	0.0170	1.0826	0.8410
CC03 10 10	0.044	49.6	5.76	0.8380	0.0211	1.0776	0.8380
CC03 10 11	0.044	47.1	5.24	0.8348	0.0256	1.0721	0.8348
CC03 10 12	0.044	44.8	4.81	0.8313	0.0306	1.0661	0.8313
CC03 10 13	0.044	42.7	4.45	0.8274	0.0361	1.0596	0.8274
CC03 10 14	0.044	40.7	4.13	0.8233	0.0420	1.0525	0.8233
CC03 10 15	0.044	38.9	3.86	0.8188	0.0485	1.0449	0.8188
CC03 10 16	0.044	37.2	3.63	0.8140	0.0555	1.0368	0.8140
CC03 10 17	0.044	35.6	3.42	0.8090	0.0630	1.0282	0.8090
CC03 10 18	0.044	34.1	3.24	0.8036	0.0712	1.0190	0.8036
CC03 10 19	0.044	32.7	3.07	0.7979	0.0798	1.0094	0.7979
CC03 10 20	0.044	31.3	2.92	0.7920	0.0892	0.9992	0.7920
CC03 10 21	0.044	30.0	2.79	0.7857	0.0991	0.9885	0.7857
CC03 10 22	0.044	28.8	2.67	0.7791	0.1097	0.9774	0.7791

FILTER	Ap	As	ws	L1	L2	C2	L3

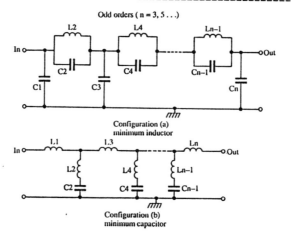

Odd orders (n = 3, 5 . . .)

Configuration (a)
minimum inductor

Configuration (b)
minimum capacitor

Figure 2.20 *Elliptic low-pass filter passive implementations*

FILTER	Ap	As	ws	C1	C2	L2	C3
CC03 20 04	0.177	79.6	14.34	1.1870	0.0032	1.1507	1.1870
CC03 20 05	0.177	73.8	11.47	1.1856	0.0050	1.1488	1.1856
CC03 20 06	0.177	69.1	9.57	1.1839	0.0072	1.1464	1.1839
CC03 20 07	0.177	65.0	8.21	1.1819	0.0098	1.1436	1.1819
CC03 20 08	0.177	61.5	7.19	1.1796	0.0128	1.1404	1.1796
CC03 20 09	0.177	58.5	6.39	1.1770	0.0162	1.1367	1.1770
CC03 20 10	0.177	55.7	5.76	1.1740	0.0200	1.1326	1.1740
CC03 20 11	0.177	53.2	5.24	1.1708	0.0243	1.1281	1.1708
CC03 20 12	0.177	50.9	4.81	1.1672	0.0290	1.1231	1.1672
CC03 20 13	0.177	48.8	4.45	1.1634	0.0342	1.1177	1.1634
CC03 20 14	0.177	46.9	4.13	1.1592	0.0398	1.1119	1.1592
CC03 20 15	0.177	45.1	3.86	1.1547	0.0458	1.1057	1.1547
CC03 20 16	0.177	43.4	3.63	1.1500	0.0524	1.0990	1.1500
CC03 20 17	0.177	41.8	3.42	1.1449	0.0594	1.0919	1.1449
CC03 20 18	0.177	40.2	3.24	1.1395	0.0669	1.0844	1.1395
CC03 20 19	0.177	38.8	3.07	1.1338	0.0749	1.0764	1.1338
CC03 20 20	0.177	37.4	2.92	1.1278	0.0834	1.0681	1.1278
CC03 20 21	0.177	36.1	2.79	1.1215	0.0925	1.0593	1.1215
CC03 20 22	0.177	34.9	2.67	1.1149	0.1021	1.0500	1.1149
CC03 20 23	0.177	33.7	2.56	1.1080	0.1123	1.0404	1.1080
CC03 50 05	1.249	82.8	11.47	2.2014	0.0060	0.9452	2.2014
CC03 50 06	1.249	78.1	9.57	2.1991	0.0087	0.9437	2.1991
CC03 50 07	1.249	74.1	8.21	2.1965	0.0118	0.9418	2.1965
CC03 50 08	1.249	70.6	7.19	2.1935	0.0155	0.9397	2.1935
CC03 50 09	1.249	67.5	6.39	2.1900	0.0196	0.9373	2.1900
CC03 50 10	1.249	64.7	5.76	2.1862	0.0243	0.9346	2.1862
CC03 50 11	1.249	62.2	5.24	2.1819	0.0294	0.9317	2.1819
CC03 50 12	1.249	60.0	4.81	2.1773	0.0351	0.9284	2.1773
CC03 50 13	1.249	57.9	4.45	2.1722	0.0413	0.9249	2.1722
CC03 50 14	1.249	55.9	4.13	2.1668	0.0480	0.9211	2.1668
CC03 50 15	1.249	54.1	3.86	2.1609	0.0553	0.9170	2.1609
CC03 50 16	1.249	52.4	3.63	2.1547	0.0630	0.9126	2.1547
CC03 50 17	1.249	50.8	3.42	2.1480	0.0714	0.9080	2.1480
CC03 50 18	1.249	49.3	3.24	2.1409	0.0803	0.9031	2.1409
CC03 50 19	1.249	47.8	3.07	2.1335	0.0898	0.8979	2.1335
CC03 50 21	1.249	45.2	2.79	2.1173	0.1105	0.8866	2.1173
CC03 50 23	1.249	42.7	2.56	2.0996	0.1336	0.8743	2.0996
CC03 50 25	1.249	40.5	2.37	2.0803	0.1594	0.8608	2.0803
CC03 50 27	1.249	38.4	2.20	2.0594	0.1878	0.8462	2.0594
CC03 50 29	1.249	36.5	2.06	2.0370	0.2192	0.8306	2.0370
FILTER	Ap	As	ws	L1	L2	C2	L3

are included in this comparatively brief set of tables. The tables are abbreviated versions of what are often published in full. A full tabulation of the CC05 20 designs, for example, contains 90 designs with A_s values ranging from 210 dB to 27.5 dB, in steps of typically 2 dB. For most realistic filter applications, the full tables therefore contain many designs which will never be used. The author has chosen twenty useful designs for each order and passband ripple value.

These odd-order filters are all designed to operate between equal terminations and are normalized in the usual way. Although the tables contain only a very small proportion of the total number of designs which have been catalogued, they represent a very useful selection which will fulfil most

Table 2.10 *Normalized component values for fifth order elliptic low-pass passive filters with passband ripples of 0.011, 0.044, 0.177 and 1.249 dB*

FILTER	Ap	As	ws	C1	C2	L2	C3	C4	L4	C5
CC05 05 13	0.011	86.4	4.45	0.7556	0.0137	1.2947	1.5584	0.0364	1.2586	0.7335
CC05 05 15	0.011	80.1	3.86	0.7519	0.0183	1.2895	1.5485	0.0489	1.2416	0.7226
CC05 05 17	0.011	74.6	3.42	0.7478	0.0236	1.2836	1.5374	0.0635	1.2221	0.7101
CC05 05 19	0.011	69.7	3.07	0.7431	0.0297	1.2768	1.5249	0.0802	1.2002	0.6959
CC05 05 21	0.011	65.3	2.79	0.7379	0.0365	1.2694	1.5112	0.0994	1.1760	0.6802
CC05 05 23	0.011	61.2	2.56	0.7321	0.0441	1.2611	1.4962	0.1210	1.1494	0.6628
CC05 05 25	0.011	57.5	2.37	0.7257	0.0524	1.2520	1.4800	0.1454	1.1205	0.6437
CC05 05 27	0.011	54.0	2.20	0.7187	0.0617	1.2421	1.4627	0.1729	1.0893	0.6229
CC05 05 29	0.011	50.8	2.06	0.7112	0.0718	1.2314	1.4444	0.2038	1.0559	0.6003
CC05 05 31	0.011	47.7	1.94	0.7030	0.0828	1.2198	1.4250	0.2384	1.0201	0.5760
CC05 05 33	0.011	44.9	1.84	0.6942	0.0948	1.2073	1.4048	0.2774	0.9822	0.5498
CC05 05 35	0.011	42.1	1.74	0.6847	0.1078	1.1938	1.3837	0.3214	0.9422	0.5217
CC05 05 37	0.011	39.5	1.66	0.6746	0.1220	1.1794	1.3619	0.3712	0.9001	0.4917
CC05 05 39	0.011	37.1	1.59	0.6637	0.1374	1.1638	1.3396	0.4278	0.8559	0.4595
CC05 05 41	0.011	34.7	1.52	0.6521	0.1541	1.1472	1.3168	0.4924	0.8099	0.4252
CC05 05 43	0.011	32.4	1.47	0.6397	0.1722	1.1292	1.2937	0.5669	0.7620	0.3885
CC05 05 45	0.011	30.2	1.41	0.6265	0.1920	1.1099	1.2706	0.6535	0.7125	0.3494
CC05 05 47	0.011	28.0	1.37	0.6124	0.2135	1.0891	1.2478	0.7550	0.6614	0.3075
CC05 05 49	0.011	26.0	1.33	0.5973	0.2372	1.0665	1.2254	0.8756	0.6090	0.2628
CC05 05 51	0.011	23.9	1.29	0.5813	0.2632	1.0420	1.2039	1.0206	0.5556	0.2147
CC05 10 15	0.044	86.2	3.86	0.9590	0.0175	1.3523	1.7601	0.0464	1.3101	0.9312
CC05 10 17	0.044	80.7	3.42	0.9550	0.0226	1.3466	1.7480	0.0601	1.2925	0.9192
CC05 10 19	0.044	75.7	3.07	0.9504	0.0283	1.3401	1.7344	0.0757	1.2728	0.9057
CC05 10 21	0.044	71.3	2.79	0.9452	0.0348	1.3329	1.7193	0.0935	1.2509	0.8906
CC05 10 23	0.044	67.3	2.56	0.9395	0.0420	1.3250	1.7029	0.1134	1.2269	0.8741
CC05 10 25	0.044	63.5	2.37	0.9333	0.0499	1.3162	1.6851	0.1358	1.2007	0.8560
CC05 10 27	0.044	60.1	2.20	0.9265	0.0587	1.3067	1.6659	0.1607	1.1725	0.8363
CC05 10 29	0.044	56.8	2.06	0.9191	0.0682	1.2964	1.6455	0.1884	1.1423	0.8151
CC05 10 31	0.044	53.8	1.94	0.9111	0.0786	1.2852	1.6238	0.2192	1.1100	0.7923
CC05 10 33	0.044	50.9	1.84	0.9024	0.0899	1.2732	1.6008	0.2534	1.0757	0.7678
CC05 10 35	0.044	48.2	1.74	0.8932	0.1022	1.2603	1.5768	0.2914	1.0395	0.7418
CC05 10 37	0.044	45.6	1.66	0.8833	0.1155	1.2465	1.5516	0.3337	1.0014	0.7140
CC05 10 39	0.044	43.1	1.59	0.8726	0.1299	1.2317	1.5254	0.3809	0.9613	0.6846
CC05 10 41	0.044	40.7	1.52	0.8613	0.1454	1.2159	1.4983	0.4338	0.9195	0.6533
CC05 10 43	0.044	38.4	1.47	0.8492	0.1623	1.1991	1.4703	0.4933	0.8759	0.6203
CC05 10 45	0.044	36.2	1.41	0.8363	0.1805	1.1810	1.4416	0.5606	0.8307	0.5853
CC05 10 47	0.044	34.1	1.37	0.8226	0.2003	1.1617	1.4123	0.6372	0.7839	0.5483
CC05 10 49	0.044	32.0	1.33	0.8080	0.2217	1.1410	1.3285	0.7251	0.7355	0.5092
CC05 10 51	0.044	30.0	1.29	0.7924	0.2451	1.1188	1.3524	0.8269	0.6858	0.4679
CC05 10 53	0.044	28.0	1.25	0.7758	0.2708	1.0950	1.3223	0.9460	0.6349	0.4241
CC05 20 20	0.177	79.6	2.92	1.2751	0.0321	1.3129	2.0418	0.0852	1.2498	1.2249
CC05 20 22	0.177	75.4	2.67	1.2694	0.0390	1.3059	2.0238	0.1039	1.2299	1.2088
CC05 20 24	0.177	71.5	2.46	1.2631	0.0467	1.2982	2.0041	0.1249	1.2081	1.1910
CC05 20 26	0.177	67.9	2.28	1.2526	0.0551	1.2899	1.9828	0.1482	1.1845	1.1718
CC05 20 28	0.177	64.6	2.13	1.2488	0.0644	1.2808	1.9600	0.1740	1.1591	1.1511
CC05 20 30	0.177	61.4	2.00	1.2407	0.0745	1.2709	1.9355	0.2024	1.1320	1.1287
CC05 20 32	0.177	58.5	1.89	1.2319	0.0854	1.2603	1.9095	0.2337	1.1031	1.1049
CC05 20 34	0.177	55.7	1.79	1.2225	0.0973	1.2489	1.8820	0.2682	1.0724	1.0794
CC05 20 36	0.177	53.0	1.70	1.2124	0.1102	1.2367	1.8531	0.3061	1.0401	1.0524
CC05 20 38	0.177	50.5	1.62	1.2017	0.1241	1.2236	1.8227	0.3480	1.0061	1.0239
CC05 20 40	0.177	48.1	1.56	1.1902	0.1391	1.2097	1.7909	0.3941	0.9705	0.9937
CC05 20 42	0.177	45.7	1.49	1.1779	0.1553	1.1949	1.7578	0.4451	0.9334	0.9619
CC05 20 44	0.177	43.5	1.44	1.1648	0.1728	1.1790	1.7235	0.5017	0.8946	0.9284
CC05 20 46	0.177	41.3	1.39	1.1509	0.1917	1.1622	1.6879	0.5648	0.8544	0.8933
CC05 20 47	0.177	40.2	1.37	1.1436	0.2017	1.1534	1.6697	0.5990	0.8338	0.8750
CC05 20 49	0.177	38.2	1.33	1.1283	0.2229	1.1348	1.6324	0.6739	0.7914	0.8373
CC05 20 51	0.177	36.1	1.29	1.1121	0.2460	1.1151	1.5941	0.7584	0.7477	0.7977
CC05 20 53	0.177	34.1	1.25	1.0948	0.2910	1.0940	1.5549	0.8547	0.7028	0.7562
CC05 20 55	0.177	32.2	1.22	1.0763	0.2983	1.0715	1.5150	0.9652	0.6567	0.7127
CC05 20 57	0.177	30.3	1.19	1.0567	0.3282	1.0473	1.4743	1.0934	0.6095	0.6671
CC05 50 19	1.249	90.9	3.07	2.2865	0.0375	1.0138	3.0906	0.0988	0.9760	2.2278
CC05 50 21	1.249	86.5	2.79	2.2791	0.0460	1.0090	3.0654	0.1214	0.9630	2.2076
CC05 50 23	1.249	82.4	2.56	2.2709	0.0554	1.0038	3.0378	0.1467	0.9488	2.1854
CC05 50 25	1.249	78.7	2.37	2.2620	0.0659	0.9980	3.0078	0.1747	0.9333	2.1612
CC05 50 27	1.249	75.2	2.20	2.2522	0.0773	0.9916	2.9753	0.2056	0.9165	2.1350
CC05 50 29	1.249	72.0	2.06	2.2415	0.0898	0.9848	2.9405	0.2395	0.8986	2.1069
CC05 50 31	1.249	69.0	1.94	2.2300	0.1034	0.9774	2.9032	0.2767	0.8794	2.0768
CC05 50 33	1.249	66.1	1.84	2.2177	0.1181	0.9695	2.8636	0.3173	0.8591	2.0448
CC05 50 35	1.249	63.4	1.74	2.2044	0.1340	0.9610	2.8217	0.3617	0.8376	2.0108
CC05 50 37	1.249	60.8	1.66	2.1902	0.1512	0.9519	2.7775	0.4101	0.8149	1.9749
CC05 50 39	1.249	58.3	1.59	2.1751	0.1698	0.9421	2.7310	0.4629	0.7911	1.9371
CC05 50 41	1.249	55.9	1.52	2.1590	0.1898	0.9318	2.6822	0.5206	0.7662	1.8974
CC05 50 43	1.249	53.6	1.47	2.1418	0.2113	0.9208	2.6312	0.5837	0.7402	1.8558
CC05 50 45	1.249	51.4	1.41	2.1235	0.2345	0.9909	2.5780	0.6529	0.7132	1.8122
CC05 50 47	1.249	49.3	1.37	2.1041	0.2594	0.8967	2.5226	0.7290	0.6851	1.7667
CC05 50 49	1.249	47.2	1.33	2.0835	0.2864	0.8835	2.4652	0.8129	0.6561	1.7193
CC05 50 51	1.249	45.2	1.29	2.0615	0.3154	0.8695	2.4056	0.9059	0.6260	1.6699
CC05 50 53	1.249	43.2	1.25	2.0383	0.3469	0.8546	2.3439	1.0094	0.5950	1.6186
CC05 50 55	1.249	41.2	1.22	2.0135	0.3810	0.8387	2.2803	1.1254	0.5632	1.5653
CC05 50 57	1.249	39.3	1.19	1.9872	0.4182	0.8219	2.2146	1.2564	0.5304	1.5099
FILTER	Ap	As	ws	L1	L2	C2	L3	L4	C4	L5

Table 2.11 *Normalized component values for seventh order elliptic low-pass filters with passband ripples of 0.011, 0.044, 0.177 and 1.249 dB*

FILTER	Ap	As	ws	C1	C2	L2	C3	C4	L4	C5	C6	L6	C7
CC07 05 26	0.011	93.2	2.28	0.7835	0.0289	1.3621	1.6383	0.1268	1.4475	1.5961	0.0968	1.2637	0.7204
CC07 05 28	0.011	88.5	2.13	0.7797	0.0338	1.3564	1.6194	0.1486	1.4181	1.5709	0.1136	1.2424	0.7063
CC07 05 30	0.011	84.1	2.00	0.7755	0.0391	1.3502	1.5992	0.1725	1.3868	1.5440	0.1322	1.2196	0.6910
CC07 05 32	0.011	80.0	1.89	0.7709	0.0447	1.3435	1.5776	0.1987	1.3534	1.5155	0.1527	1.1951	0.6745
CC07 05 34	0.011	76.1	1.79	0.7660	0.0510	1.3362	1.5547	0.2274	1.3181	1.4854	0.1752	1.1690	0.6569
CC07 05 36	0.011	72.4	1.70	0.7607	0.0578	1.3284	1.5305	0.2589	1.2809	1.4537	0.2000	1.1413	0.6379
CC07 05 38	0.011	68.8	1.62	0.7549	0.0651	1.3200	1.5049	0.2933	1.2418	1.4206	0.2272	1.1119	0.6177
CC07 05 40	0.011	65.4	1.56	0.7488	0.0729	1.3110	1.4780	0.3310	1.2009	1.3860	0.2572	1.0810	0.5962
CC07 05 42	0.011	62.1	1.49	0.7422	0.0814	1.3013	1.4498	0.3723	1.1581	1.3502	0.2902	1.0484	0.5732
CC07 05 44	0.011	59.0	1.44	0.7351	0.0906	1.2910	1.4203	0.4179	1.1136	1.3130	0.3268	1.0141	0.5487
CC07 05 46	0.011	55.9	1.39	0.7276	0.1004	1.2798	1.3895	0.4681	1.0674	1.2747	0.3673	0.9783	0.5228
CC07 05 48	0.011	53.0	1.35	0.7194	0.1111	1.2679	1.3573	0.5238	1.0195	1.2354	0.4124	0.9407	0.4951
CC07 05 50	0.011	50.1	1.31	0.7107	0.1226	1.2552	1.3239	0.5859	0.9699	1.1951	0.4620	0.9015	0.4657
CC07 05 52	0.011	47.3	1.27	0.7013	0.1351	1.2414	1.2891	0.6554	0.9177	1.1540	0.5194	0.8607	0.4344
CC07 05 54	0.011	44.6	1.24	0.6911	0.1486	1.2266	1.2531	0.7340	0.8660	1.1123	0.5836	0.8181	0.4010
CC07 05 56	0.011	41.9	1.21	0.6802	0.1634	1.2107	1.2157	0.8237	0.8117	1.0702	0.6567	0.7739	0.3654
CC07 05 57	0.011	40.5	1.19	0.6744	0.1713	1.2023	1.1965	0.8734	0.7840	1.0490	0.6973	0.7512	0.3467
CC07 05 58	0.011	39.2	1.18	0.6684	0.1795	1.1935	1.1770	0.9269	0.7559	1.0278	0.7409	0.7280	0.3273
CC07 05 59	0.011	37.9	1.17	0.6622	0.1882	1.1843	1.1572	0.9848	0.7275	1.0066	0.7880	0.7045	0.3072
CC07 05 60	0.011	36.6	1.15	0.6556	0.1972	1.1747	1.1371	1.0475	0.6988	0.9854	0.8389	0.6805	0.2864
CC07 10 30	0.044	90.2	2.00	0.9785	0.0379	1.3920	1.7744	0.1724	1.3879	1.7148	0.1266	1.2737	0.8971
CC07 10 32	0.044	86.1	1.89	0.9740	0.0435	1.3855	1.7516	0.1983	1.3565	1.6843	0.1459	1.2511	0.8812
CC07 10 34	0.044	82.1	1.79	0.9691	0.0495	1.3785	1.7275	0.2266	1.3232	1.6520	0.1669	1.2270	0.8642
CC07 10 36	0.044	78.4	1.70	0.9638	0.0560	1.3710	1.7019	0.2574	1.2881	1.6180	0.1900	1.2015	0.8460
CC07 10 38	0.044	74.9	1.62	0.9581	0.0630	1.3629	1.6749	0.2911	1.2512	1.5823	0.2151	1.1744	0.8266
CC07 10 40	0.044	71.5	1.56	0.9520	0.0706	1.3542	1.6465	0.3278	1.2126	1.5449	0.2426	1.1458	0.8060
CC07 10 42	0.044	68.2	1.49	0.9455	0.0788	1.3449	1.6168	0.3678	1.1723	1.5060	0.2727	1.1156	0.7842
CC07 10 44	0.044	65.0	1.44	0.9385	0.0876	1.3350	1.5857	0.4117	1.1303	1.4655	0.3057	1.0840	0.7610
CC07 10 46	0.044	62.0	1.39	0.9310	0.0971	1.3243	1.5532	0.4598	1.0867	1.4236	0.3420	1.0508	0.7364
CC07 10 48	0.044	59.0	1.35	0.9229	0.1073	1.3129	1.5193	0.5127	1.0416	1.3803	0.3818	1.0160	0.7104
CC07 10 50	0.044	56.2	1.31	0.9143	0.1183	1.3006	1.4840	0.5711	0.9949	1.3357	0.4259	0.9796	0.6829
CC07 10 52	0.044	53.4	1.27	0.9050	0.1302	1.2875	1.4474	0.6360	0.9468	1.2899	0.4748	0.9416	0.6538
CC07 10 53	0.044	52.0	1.25	0.9002	0.1366	1.2806	1.4286	0.6712	0.9221	1.2666	0.5013	0.9220	0.6386
CC07 10 54	0.044	50.6	1.24	0.8951	0.1432	1.2735	1.4094	0.7085	0.8972	1.2430	0.5293	0.9020	0.6230
CC07 10 55	0.044	49.3	1.22	0.8898	0.1500	1.2660	1.3898	0.7481	0.8718	1.2191	0.5590	0.8815	0.6069
CC07 10 56	0.044	47.9	1.21	0.8844	0.1572	1.2583	1.3700	0.7901	0.8462	1.1950	0.5905	0.8607	0.5903
CC07 10 57	0.044	46.6	1.19	0.8787	0.1647	1.2503	1.3497	0.8349	0.8202	1.1707	0.6240	0.8394	0.5733
CC07 10 58	0.044	45.3	1.18	0.8728	0.1725	1.2420	1.3291	0.8827	0.7938	1.1462	0.6596	0.8177	0.5557
CC07 10 59	0.044	44.0	1.17	0.8666	0.1807	1.2333	1.3082	0.9339	0.7671	1.1215	0.6977	0.7956	0.5375
CC07 10 60	0.044	42.7	1.15	0.8602	0.1892	1.2243	1.2869	0.9889	0.7402	1.0966	0.7384	0.7731	0.5188
CC07 20 32	0.177	92.2	1.89	1.2968	0.0449	1.3214	2.0288	0.2106	1.2772	1.9524	0.1490	1.2749	1.2015
CC07 20 34	0.177	88.3	1.79	1.2916	0.0511	1.3349	2.0019	0.2404	1.2473	1.9161	0.1702	1.2036	1.1840
CC07 20 36	0.177	84.6	1.70	1.2860	0.0578	1.3280	1.9734	0.2727	1.2158	1.8778	0.1932	1.1811	1.1653
CC07 20 38	0.177	81.0	1.62	1.2800	0.0650	1.3206	1.9434	0.3079	1.1826	1.8375	0.2183	1.1572	1.1454
CC07 20 40	0.177	77.6	1.56	1.2736	0.0728	1.3127	1.9118	0.3462	1.1480	1.7952	0.2456	1.1319	1.1243
CC07 20 42	0.177	74.4	1.49	1.2667	0.0812	1.3042	1.8787	0.3879	1.1117	1.7511	0.2753	1.1053	1.1019
CC07 20 44	0.177	71.2	1.44	1.2592	0.0903	1.2951	1.8440	0.4332	1.0741	1.7052	0.3076	1.0774	1.0783
CC07 20 46	0.177	68.2	1.39	1.2513	0.1000	1.2853	1.8079	0.4824	1.0349	1.6574	0.3429	1.0480	1.0533
CC07 20 48	0.177	65.2	1.35	1.2427	0.1105	1.2749	1.7702	0.5370	0.9944	1.6079	0.3814	1.0172	1.0270
CC07 20 50	0.177	62.6	1.31	1.2336	0.1218	1.2638	1.7309	0.5966	0.9525	1.5567	0.4235	0.9850	0.9992
CC07 20 51	0.177	60.9	1.29	1.2288	0.1277	1.2577	1.7107	0.6286	0.9311	1.5305	0.4462	0.9684	0.9848
CC07 20 52	0.177	59.5	1.27	1.2239	0.1339	1.2518	1.6901	0.6622	0.9093	1.5039	0.4699	0.9514	0.9699
CC07 20 53	0.177	58.1	1.25	1.2187	0.1404	1.2456	1.6692	0.6977	0.8872	1.4769	0.4948	0.9340	0.9547
CC07 20 54	0.177	56.8	1.24	1.2134	0.1471	1.2391	1.6478	0.7351	0.8648	1.4495	0.5211	0.9163	0.9391
CC07 20 55	0.177	55.4	1.22	1.2078	0.1541	1.2323	1.6261	0.7745	0.8421	1.4218	0.5487	0.8981	0.9230
CC07 20 56	0.177	54.1	1.21	1.2021	0.1614	1.2253	1.6039	0.8163	0.8190	1.3937	0.5778	0.8796	0.9065
CC07 20 57	0.177	52.8	1.19	1.1961	0.1690	1.2181	1.5814	0.8605	0.7957	1.3652	0.6085	0.8607	0.8896
CC07 20 58	0.177	51.4	1.18	1.1899	0.1770	1.2106	1.5584	0.9075	0.7721	1.3364	0.6411	0.8414	0.8722
CC07 20 59	0.177	50.1	1.17	1.1834	0.1853	1.2028	1.5351	0.9576	0.7482	1.3072	0.6755	0.8217	0.8544
CC07 20 60	0.177	48.8	1.15	1.1768	0.1939	1.1947	1.5113	1.0110	0.7240	1.2778	0.7121	0.8017	0.8360
CC07 50 34	1.249	97.3	1.79	2.2920	0.0672	1.0145	2.9579	0.3261	0.9193	2.8338	0.2214	0.9252	2.1511
CC07 50 36	1.249	93.6	1.70	2.2843	0.0760	1.0095	2.9174	0.3696	0.8971	2.7787	0.2509	0.9096	2.1264
CC07 50 38	1.249	90.1	1.62	2.2760	0.0855	1.0042	2.8746	0.4168	0.8737	2.7207	0.2829	0.8931	2.1002
CC07 50 40	1.249	86.7	1.56	2.2672	0.0958	0.9984	2.8297	0.4680	0.8493	2.6599	0.3175	0.8756	2.0725
CC07 50 42	1.249	83.4	1.49	2.2577	0.1068	0.9923	2.7825	0.5235	0.8237	2.5962	0.3550	0.8572	2.0432
CC07 50 44	1.249	80.2	1.44	2.2475	0.1186	0.9858	2.7332	0.5837	0.7972	2.5297	0.3956	0.8378	2.0122
CC07 50 46	1.249	77.2	1.39	2.2367	0.1313	0.9788	2.6817	0.6492	0.7696	2.4605	0.4396	0.8174	1.9796
CC07 50 48	1.249	74.2	1.35	2.2251	0.1450	0.9713	2.6280	0.7206	0.7410	2.3885	0.4873	0.7961	1.9454
CC07 50 49	1.249	72.8	1.33	2.2190	0.1522	0.9674	2.6004	0.7587	0.7264	2.3516	0.5127	0.7850	1.9276
CC07 50 50	1.249	71.4	1.31	2.2127	0.1597	0.9633	2.5722	0.7986	0.7115	2.3139	0.5392	0.7737	1.9093
CC07 50 51	1.249	69.9	1.29	2.2061	0.1675	0.9592	2.5434	0.8404	0.6964	2.2757	0.5669	0.7622	1.8907
CC07 50 52	1.249	68.6	1.27	2.1994	0.1756	0.9548	2.5141	0.8842	0.6810	2.2367	0.5958	0.7504	1.8715
CC07 50 53	1.249	67.2	1.25	2.1924	0.1840	0.9503	2.4843	0.9302	0.6654	2.1972	0.6260	0.7383	1.8519
CC07 50 54	1.249	65.8	1.24	2.1851	0.1928	0.9457	2.4539	0.9785	0.6497	2.1570	0.6577	0.7260	1.8318
CC07 50 55	1.249	64.5	1.22	2.1776	0.2019	0.9409	2.4229	1.0293	0.6336	2.1161	0.6908	0.7134	1.8112
CC07 50 56	1.249	63.1	1.21	2.1699	0.2113	0.9359	2.3914	1.0828	0.6174	2.0747	0.7256	0.7005	1.7901
CC07 50 57	1.249	61.8	1.19	2.1618	0.2212	0.9307	2.3593	1.1394	0.6010	2.0326	0.7621	0.6873	1.7685
CC07 50 58	1.249	60.5	1.18	2.1534	0.2315	0.9254	2.3266	1.1991	0.5843	1.9899	0.8004	0.6739	1.7463
CC07 50 59	1.249	59.2	1.17	2.1447	0.2422	0.9199	2.2933	1.2625	0.5675	1.9466	0.8408	0.6602	1.7236
CC07 50 60	1.249	57.8	1.15	2.1357	0.2535	0.9141	2.2594	1.3297	0.5504	1.9028	0.8835	0.6462	1.7004
FILTER	Ap	As	ws	L1	L2	C2	L3	L4	C4	L5	L6	C6	L7

requirements. More extensive catalogues will be found in references 12, 13, 14, and 15. An example illustrating the use of the tables is given later in this chapter, in the section on frequency and impedance scaling.

The identifying code given for each filter is of the form CC $n \rho \theta$. CC is an abbreviation for Cauer-Chebyshev, acknowledging the contribution Cauer made to the mathematics describing their nature and that they are a sub-group of the Chebyshev family of responses; the order of the filter; the reflection coefficient as a truncated percentage (as for the Chebyshev filters); and finally the modular angle, θ, (in degrees) defined as

$$\theta = \sin^{-1}\left(\frac{1}{\omega_s}\right) \tag{2.12}$$

where ω_s is the frequency at which A_s is the first attained.

For example, if an elliptic filter achieves its A_s value at $\omega_s = 1.325\,\text{rad/s}$, then $\theta = 49°$ and so a third order 0.18 dB passband ripple filter with this value of ω_s can be referred to as CC03 20 49. Similarly, a fifth-order 0.28 dB elliptic filter with a modular angle of 45° can be called CC05 24 45.

The Bessel response

So far, nothing has been said about the phase relationship of output to input of a low-pass filter. In most applications it is the amplitude response of a filter which is important, and the Butterworth, Chebyshev and elliptic approximations optimize their amplitude responses to some desirable aspects of the ideal at the expense of deviating from the ideal phase response. What is the ideal low-pass phase response? Figure 2.21 shows how the phase of an output signal should vary with respect to the input as the input is swept in frequency. The response is an upward sloping straight line, indicating that the phase shift should vary linearly with input frequency up to the cut-off frequency. Beyond cut-off, the phase response is meaningless because the ideal low-pass filter passes no signal whatsoever outside the passband. This implies that all signals within the passband should suffer the same time delay through the filter, and a line of constant time delay, T seconds, is also shown on Fig. 2.21. This is a difficult concept to grasp and is best illustrated by reference to an example using sine-wave inputs and outputs.

Figure 2.22 shows two sine waves, of 1 kHz and 2 kHz, applied to the input of an ideal low-pass filter (whose cut-off frequency is greater than 2 kHz) and the resulting output waveforms. Because the phase shift varies linearly with frequency, the 2 kHz input suffers twice the phase shift of the 1 kHz input. In

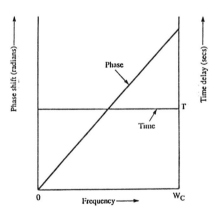

Figure 2.21 *Phase shift and time delay as functions of frequency for an ideal low-pass filter*

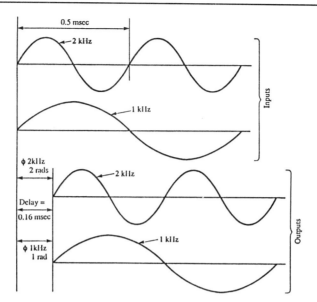

Figure 2.22 *Input and output waveforms for 1 KHz and 2 KHz sine waves through a linear phase shift filter. Though the time delay is identical for both signals the 2 KHz sine wave suffers twice the phase shift of the 1 KHz sine wave*

the diagram, the 2 kHz signal is phase shifted by about a third of a cycle, that is about 2 radians, whereas the 1 kHz signal is shifted by half this amount, about 1 radian. Both signals have been delayed by the same time period, approximately 0.16 ms; therefore, if the signals were in phase at the input of the filter they are still in phase at the output. For voice transmission applications this linear phase response is relatively unimportant. For data transmission, however, a linear phase response is important to prevent pulse distortion, and therefore linear-phase filters are often used.

One such linear-phase filter is the Bessel approximation (also called the Thompson approximation), optimized for phase rather than amplitude response. The Bessel approximation results in a low-Q filter and the amplitude roll-off is quite modest compared with even a Butterworth filter. The initial stopband attenuation can be approximated by:

$$A = 3 \left(\frac{\omega}{\omega_c} \right)^2 \quad \text{dB} \tag{2.13}$$

for any order, up to approximately $\omega/\omega_c = 2$.

For values of ω/ω_c greater than 2 a straight-line approximation of 6 dB per octave per element can be made. Figure 2.23 shows the passband amplitude response of Bessel filters for $n = 2$ to 7. The responses are so similar that they can be represented by the same curve. Figure 2.24 shows a family of curves beyond cut-off for increasing values of n.

As in the case of Chebyshev filters, there is some confusion with Bessel filters over the definition of the cut-off frequency. Since the important feature of a Bessel filter is the constant time delay, it is possible to normalize this delay to 1 second and calculate component values for 1 Ω source and termination impedances and 1 second delay[16]. Alternativeiy, the Butterworth defi-

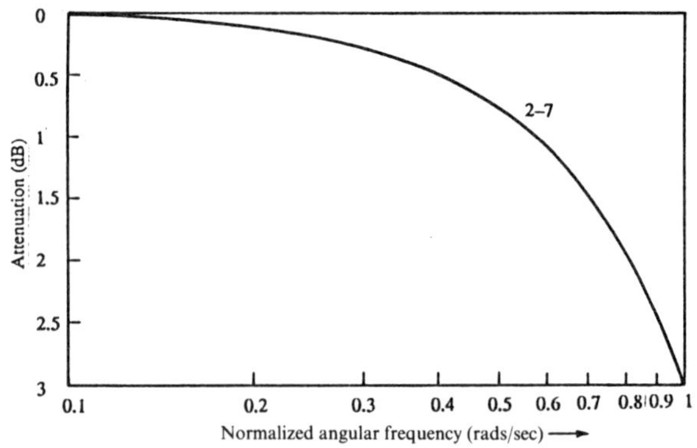

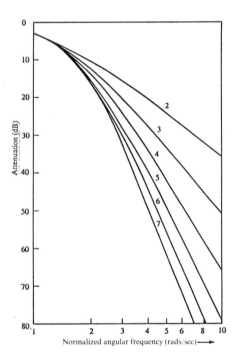

Figure 2.23 *Bessel low-pass filter passband response for n = 2 to 7. The response is normalized to have a 3.01 dB cut-off angular frequency of 1 rad/sec*

Figure 2.24 *Stopband response of Bessel low-pass filters for n = 2 to 7, assuming an attenuation at cut-off of 3 dB*

nition of cut-off, the 3 dB attenuation frequency, can be used[17,18,19] and, of course, component values obtained for these two methods are different. Since in many applications the concern is that the time delay through the filter is constant, and not what its absolute value is, the 3 dB attenuation definition will be used here. This has the advantage of allowing the cut-off frequency to be set to benefit from the modest, but still useful, attenuation characteristics of the filter.

Table 2.12 shows normalized component values for the passive implementation of Bessel low-pass filters for $n = 2$ to 7. These designs are normalized for 1 Ω source and termination impedances and a 3 dB cut-off frequency

Table 2.12 *Bessel low-pass LC element values*

FILTER	ORDER	C1	L2	C3	L4	C5	L6	C7
G02	2	0.5755	2.1478					
G03	3	0.3374	0.9705	2.2034				
G04	4	0.2334	0.6725	1.0815	2.2404			
G05	5	0.1743	0.5072	0.8040	1.1110	2.2582		
G06	6	0.1365	0.4002	0.6392	0.8538	1.1126	2.2645	
G07	7	0.1106	0.3259	0.5249	0.7020	0.8690	1.1052	2.2659
FILTER	ORDER	L1	C2	L3	C4	L5	C6	L7

of 1 rad/s. The circuit configuration for these filters is identical to the Butterworth and Chebyshev filters, and the component designations again refer to Fig. 2.10.

As with the Butterworth approximation only the order of a Bessel filter needs to be stated to fully describe the nature of its response. To avoid duplicating the initial letter of the Butterworth filters, the Gaussian initial letter is used here for Bessel filters, as Bessel filters are in the Gaussian family. The code used to identify a Bessel filter is therefore G*n*. A second-order Bessel filter can therefore be described as G02, a third order as G03, and so on.

Comparison of the low-pass approximations

Although comparisons between the Butterworth, Chebyshev, elliptic and Bessel responses have been made as the approximations have been considered individually, it is useful to take one example of each type and plot them on the same set of axes to allow a direct comparison to be made. To ensure that a fair comparison is being made the order of the responses should be the same and the Chebyshev and elliptic responses should have the same value of passband ripple. On Fig. 2.25 the stopband responses of B05, C05 20, CC05 20 38 and G05 are shown.

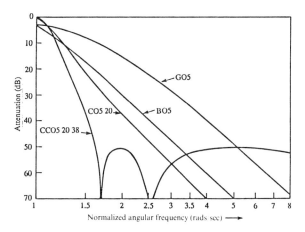

Figure 2.25 *Comparison of the stopband responses of four low-pass filters. Responses plotted are for B05, G05, C05 20 and CC05 20 38*

Other approximations

Four named approximations to the ideal low-pass filter have been described in this chapter, but these do not represent by any means the only approximations which are available. Some others which may be encountered but which cannot be discussed in detail here are: the inverse Chebyshev filter, having a Butterworth-like response in the passband and an elliptic-like response in the stopband; the transitional filter, being a compromise between the attenuation characteristics of the Butterworth approximation and the phase response of the Bessel approximation; the Gaussian filter, having no overshoot in its transient response; the Legendre filter, being a compromise between the Butterworth and Chebyshev passband responses; and the equi-ripple phase-error filter, being similar to the Bessel filter but allowing the phase response to have ripples.

Frequency and impedance scaling

Once a set of normalized component values have been selected from a catalogue of standard designs or calculated, the next step is to transform the values to give a filter which has the cut-off frequency and impedance level of the original specification. This process is known as scaling or denormalization. The following formulae are used to scale capacitors and inductors respectively:

$$C = C_n \times \frac{1}{2\pi f R} \tag{2.14}$$

and

$$L = L_n \times \frac{R}{2\pi f} \tag{2.15}$$

where C is the final capacitor value,
L is the final inductor value,
C_n is the $1\,\Omega$, $1\,\text{rad/s}$ capacitor value,
L_n is the $1\,\Omega$, $1\,\text{rad/s}$ inductor value,
R is the final impedance value,
f is the final frequency.

The scaling process is best illustrated with examples and we are now in a position to follow through the design of low-pass filters from the specification stage to the final idealized component values.

Consider the following specification: a low-pass filter is required with a cut-off frequency of 3.4 kHz; it must achieve an attenuation of 40 dB by 5 kHz, and the attenuation must not fall below this figure in the stopband. The permitted passband ripple is 0.2 dB and the filter must work with source and termination impedances of 1 kΩ.

Because ripple is permitted in the passband, either a Chebyshev or an elliptic filter could be used. Because there is no requirement for the stopband attenuation to increase monotonically an elliptic filter is the best choice since it exhibits a more rapid roll-off. The stopband attenuation frequency must first be normalized by dividing 5 kHz by 3.4 kHz (the cut-off frequency) to give $\omega_s = 1.471$ rad/s. To assess the order of filter required, Fig. 2.19 can be consulted. From this diagram the order required lies between 4 and 5, and so a fifth-order filter must be used.

From Table 2.10, three filters are possible candidates for this specification.

- CC05 20 47 has 0.18 dB of passband ripple, slightly less than the 0.2 dB allowed, and achieves 40.2 dB attenuation at 1.36 rad/s (4.65 kHz when denormalized).
- CC05 20 42 also has less passband ripple than allowed and has a minimum stopband attenuation of 45.7 dB, achieved at 1.49 rad/s (5.083 kHz).
- CC05 10 41 has a passband ripple of 0.044 dB, much less than permitted, and achieves an attenuation of 40.7 dB at 1.52 rad/s (5.18 kHz).

This demonstrates a dilemma which often faces the filter designer when using a fairly limited catalogue: there may be several potential solutions to a specification, each more or less meeting the specification and offering both advantages and disadvantages over its rivals. The skill of the designer must be used to decide the relative importance of the parameters of the specification. An exact solution to a requirement is most unlikely.

In this example we will select CC05 20 47, choosing to take advantage of the lower than specified start of stopband frequency. Figure 2.26 (a) shows the normalized minimum-inductor implementation and Fig. 2.26 (b) shows the minimum-capacitor version of this filter. Using equation 2.14, C_1 of the minimum-inductor implementation can be scaled to its 3.4 kHz, 1 kΩ value.

$$C_1 = 1.1436 \times \frac{1}{2 \times \pi \times 3400 \times 1000} = 53.53 \text{ nF}$$

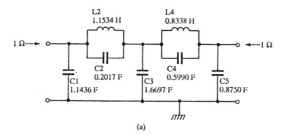

(a)

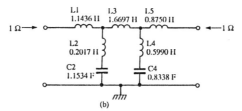

(b)

Figure 2.26 *Circuit diagrams of CC05 20 47 with normalized component values.*
a) Is the minimum component implementation
b) Is the minimum capacitor implementation
a) and b) are duals of each other, meaning that they have identical performances

Similarly, using equation 2.15, L_2 becomes

$$L_2 = 1.1534 \times \frac{1000}{2 \times \pi \times 3400} = 53.99\,\text{mH}$$

Repeating the scaling process for all the components of the filter, the denormalized designs shown in Fig. 2.27 (a) and (b) are obtained: these two configurations have identical performances in all respects. Normally, if the low-pass filter is to be implemented, rather than being a prototype for transformation (as will be described in Chapter 3), the minimum-inductor implementation would be used. Clearly, the exact component values shown in Fig. 2.27 cannot easily be obtained and Chapter 6 shows the effect on performance of using real components.

Now consider another specification: a low-pass filter is required with a cut-off frequency of 2.2 MHz, it must achieve an attenuation of 60 dB by 4.4 MHz, and the attenuation must then continue to rise. 1 dB of passband ripple is permitted and the source and termination impedances must be 50Ω.

Again because ripple in the passband is permitted, a Chebyshev or an elliptic filter seem likely approximations to be chosen. However, because the attenuation must increase monotonically, a Chebyshev design must be used. Normalizing the stopband attenuation frequency by dividing 4.4 MHz by 2.2 MHz gives an ω_s value of 2 rad/s. The nomograph for Chebyshev filters, Fig. 2.14, gives a rounder order for the filter of 7. Table 2.8 contains the 1 dB passband ripple filters and C07 45 seems a likely candidate to meet the specification. From equation 2.11, the attenuation of C07 45 at 2 rad/s is 68.18 dB. Since this is considerably more than the specified 60 dB it is worthwhile looking at a seventh-order filter with less passband ripple to see if one can still meet the 60 dB attenuation value. Reference to Fig. 2.14 shows that a seventh-order 0.1 dB passband-ripple filter only just fails to meet the 60 dB attenuation specification at 2 rad/s. Table 2.5 identifies this filter as C07 15. In

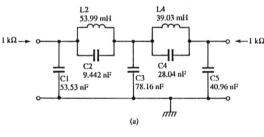

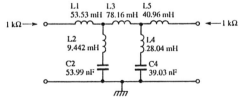

Figure 2.27 *CC05 20 47 scaled to 3.4 kHz, 1 k Ω.*
a) Is the minimum inductor implementation
b) Is the minimum capacitor implementation

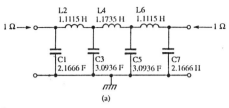

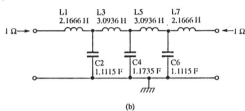

Figure 2.28 *Circuit diagrams of C07 45 with normalized component values*
a) Is the minimum inductor implementation
b) Is the minimum capacitor implementation

this example, we will choose C07 45, gaining an extra 8 dB of attenuation at 2 rad/s, because we judge that the smaller passband-ripple value available from C07 15 is not as beneficial as the extra attenuation in the stopband obtainable from C07 45.

Figure 2.28 (a) shows the normalized minimum inductor implementation and (b) shows the minimum capacitor version of this filter. Using equation 2.14, C_1 of the minimum inductor implementation can be scaled to its 2.2 MHz, 50 Ω value

$$C_1 = 2.1666 \times \frac{1}{2 \times \pi \times 2.2 \times 10^6 \times 50} = 3.135\,\text{nF}$$

Similarly, using equation 2.15,

$$L_2 = 1.1115 \times \frac{50}{2 \times \pi \times 2.2 \times 10^6} = 4.021\,\mu\text{H}$$

The denormalized filter designs are shown in Fig. 2.29 (a) and (b).

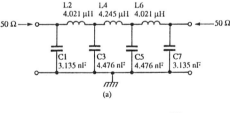

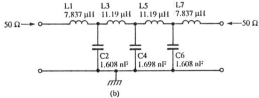

Figure 2.29 *C07 45 scaled to 2.2 MHz, 50 Ω*
a) Is the minimum inductor implementation
b) Is the minimum capacitor implementation

Summary and conclusions

The low-pass filter is an important building block in modern filter design, not only in itself but also as a starting point for transformation to other responses. When the ideal low-pass filter response is considered it is seen to be the solution to an unreasonable filtering specification and some tolerance must be allowed in the specification to make a reasonable solution possible.

Normalization is an important concept, allowing potentially an infinite number of filters with various cut-off frequencies and impedance levels to be represented by a single, normalized design. This greatly simplifies the generation and presentation of catalogues of standardized designs.

Some simple low-pass filters, containing only a few components, have been described and these are used extensively for decoupling in audio and radio circuits. When a low-pass filter consisting of a series inductor and a shunt capacitor is considered the idea of circuit Q is introduced, which can strongly influence the response of the filter.

Four named approximations to the ideal low-pass response were considered in detail. Each of these approximations optimizes some of the properties of the ideal low-pass response, causing others to deteriorate. Those considered were:

- the Butterworth approximation, a medium-Q filter, having a flat response for much of the passand and having a reasonable roll-off rate beyond cut-off;
- the Chebyshev approximation, a high-Q filter, having ripples in the passband and being capable of a faster roll-off rate than the Butterworth approximation;
- the elliptic or Cauer approximation, also a high-Q filter, having ripples in the passband and stopband and a rapid roll-off beyond cut-off;
- the Bessel or Thompson approximation, a low-Q filter, optimized for a linear phase response which can be important in data transmission systems.

The process of scaling or denormalization was described as the method of converting normalized filter designs to work at useful frequencies and impedance levels. When examples of low-pass designs were considered it was seen that the original specification can rarely be met precisely, even if exact and ideal components are assumed. In particular, when we try to satisfy a specification, a non-integral value for the order of the filter is usually obtained, which cannot be implemented in practice. Consequently, the filter order is usually rounded up and the designer has to choose how best to take advantage of the better than originally specified performance.

References

1. G.R. Jessop, G6JP, *Radio Data Reference Book*, 5th edn, 1985, RSGB. Part 3, tables 1 and 2.
2. as reference 1: part 3, tables 4, 5, 6 and 7.

3. A.I. Zverev, *Handbook of Filter Synthesis*, 1967, Wiley, p. 312–14.
4. A.B. Williams, *Electronic Filter Design Handbook*, McGraw-Hill, 1981. Table 12–2.
5. C. Bowick, *RF Circuit Design*, 1982, Sams. Table 3–2.
6. as reference 3: pages 315–22.
7. as reference 4: tables 12–27 to 12–31.
8. as reference 5: tables 3–4 to 3–7.
9. H.Y-F. Lam, *Analogue and Digital Filters: Design and Realisation*, Prentice-Hall. Tables 8–2 and 8–3.
10. P.R. Geffe, *Simplified Modern Filter Design*, John F Rider, 1963. Table A2–3.
11. G.E. Hansell, *Filter Design and Evaluation*, Van Nostrand Reinhold. Tables A1–4 to A1–9.
12. as reference 3: pages 169–289.
13. as reference 4: table 12–56.
14. as reference 10: tables A4–1 to A4–15.
15. as reference 11: tables A1–10 to A1–14.
16. as reference 9: table 8–4.
17. as reference 3: pages 323–5.
18. as reference 10: table A2–2.

3 High-pass, band-pass and band-stop filter design

Now that a number of low-pass filter approximations have been introduced, and the technique of design including denormalization described, the design of other filter responses can be tackled. The most useful responses after the low-pass response are high-pass, band-pass and band-stop, and they will be discussed in that order. One important method of design of these filter types is the transformation of low-pass prototypes. Low-pass filters are therefore not just important for use in low-pass filtering applications, but also as starting points in this transformation role; hence the fairly extensive treatment of low-pass filters in the previous chapter.

When the low-pass response was described it was introduced by simple, but nonetheless useful, examples of low-pass filters, helping to make what can be a difficult introduction to the subject much easier. Each filter response described here will be introduced in the same way. This will lead designers to realise that they probably already incorporate high-pass, band-pass and band-stop filters unknowingly in circuits, perhaps under a different guise. For example, the use of a capacitor as a DC blocking component results in a high-pass response and care must be taken that undesired effects are not introduced in this application. Once again, the emphasis will be on passive filters and the equivalent active circuit will be described in Chapter 5.

The high-pass filter response

Figure 3.1 shows the ideal high-pass amplitude response. Below the cut-off frequency ω_c, inputs are infinitely attenuated, whereas above ω_c inputs are

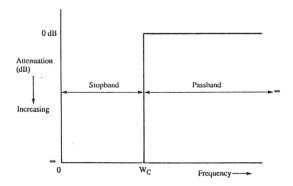

Figure 3.1 *The ideal high-pass filter amplitude response*

44

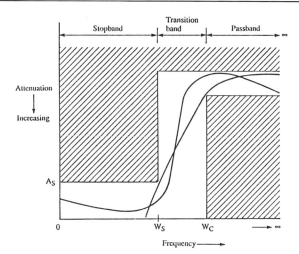

Figure 3.2 *A method of specifying a high-pass filtering amplitude requirement. The shading represents areas into which the response curve cannot enter. As in the low-pass case, an infinite number of responses can meet the specification, two of which are shown*

passed with no attenuation. The stopband is the band of frequencies below ω_c and the passband includes frequencies from ω_c up to infinite frequency.

In the same way that a more reasonable specification for a low-pass filter was shown in Chapter 2, Fig. 3.2 shows a more reasonable method of specifying the amplitude response of a high-pass filter. The stopband is not now characterized by a demand for infinite attenuation, but so long as the attenuation does not rise above some value A_s, the specification is met. Similarly, in the passband the response does not have to be perfectly flat and may have ripples if the designer can benefit from this freedom. The transition band allows a reasonable span of frequency from ω_s to ω_c for the attentuation to decrease to its passband level.

A simple high-pass filter

What is probably the simplest high-pass filter possible, a single capacitor, is shown in Fig. 3.3, driven from a voltage source and terminated by a resistor. At zero frequency, that is at DC, the capacitor blocks the transmission of any voltage from the input to the output. For AC inputs, an attenuation of the output with respect to the input will be seen because of the potential divider action occuring between the reactance of the capacitor and the load resistor. As frequency increases the reactance of the capacitor decreases and so the capacitor has less effect on the potential divider action. Eventually, at very

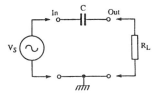

Figure 3.3 *A simple high-pass filter consisting of a single capacitor*

high frequencies, the capacitor will virtually disappear from the circuit and the output voltage will tend towards the input voltage.

The DC-blocking property of this simple circuit results in its widespread use in circuits where DC isolation is required between stages whose operating conditions need to be independent. Because the primary use of the capacitor in this application is for isolation, the high-pass nature of the circuit can easily be forgotten, resulting in unexpected, and undesirable, attenuation of lower frequencies. This is most likely to occur in audio circuits where frequencies of interest may span many octaves, and a high value for the blocking capacitor must be chosen to minimize the high-pass effect. Raising the impedance levels throughout the circuit, not normally a difficult thing to do in audio applications, will help to keep the blocking capacitor values reasonable.

High-pass filter approximations

Figure 3.4 shows the generalized response of a high-pass filter. Because several low-pass response types have been considered in detail in Chapter 2 we should be able to recognise that the response looks similar to the low-pass response of the Butterworth approximation, having no ripples in the pass-band and monotonically increasing attentuation in the stopband. If Fig. 3.4 is compared with Fig. 2.7, the responses can be seen to be symmetrical about the cut-off frequency; that is, one response can be obtained from the other by taking the inverse of frequency. If the cut-off frequency, ω_c, of the low-pass response is 1 rad/s, then ω_c for the high-pass response will also be 1 rad/s; if the frequency of high attentuation, ω_s, for the low-pass response is 2 rad/s, then ω_s for the high-pass response will be 0.5 rad/s; if the reciprocal of the frequency at which the low-pass response achieves any given attentuation is taken, that will be the frequency at which the high-pass response achieves the same attentuation.

Typical Chebyshev and elliptic high-pass filter responses are shown in Fig. 3.5 (a) and (b) respectively. A comparison of Fig. 3.5 (a) with Fig. 2.11, and Fig. 3.5 (b) with Fig. 2.16 illustrates the similarity of the low-pass and

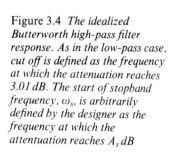

Figure 3.4 *The idealized Butterworth high-pass filter response. As in the low-pass case, cut off is defined as the frequency at which the attenuation reaches 3.01 dB. The start of stopband frequency, ω_s, is arbitrarily defined by the designer as the frequency at which the attentuation reaches A_s dB*

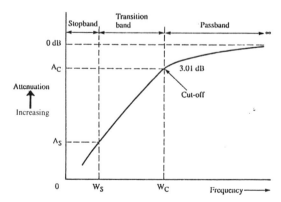

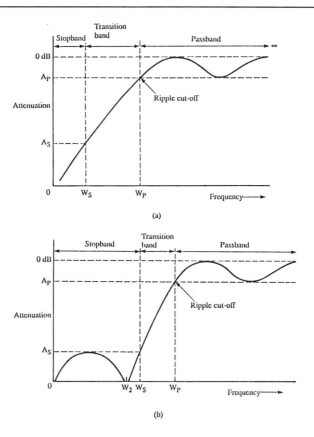

Figure 3.5 *Idealized high-pass
filter responses*
a) Is a Chebyshev response
b) Is an elliptic response

high-pass responses for a given approximation. For example, the elliptic approximation has ripples in the passband and stopband, and frequencies of infinite attentuation in the stopband (at frequencies which are inverses of each other) for both the low-pass and high-pass responses.

The low-pass to high-pass transformation

The symmetry of the low-pass and high-pass responses means that any high-pass filtering specification can be turned into an equivalent low-pass filtering specification. This allows a low-pass filter to be selected which meets the low-pass specification, and this low-pass prototype to be transformed into the required high-pass configuration, meeting the original high-pass specification. The transformation of a low-pass prototype into a high-pass filter is a simple process: in the normalized design all capacitors are replaced by inductors, all inductors are replaced by capacitors, and the transformed components have the value of the reciprocal of the original component. This transformation is illustrated in Fig. 3.6, where the low-pass prototype components have the subscript L. Composite branches, such as parallel and series combinations of capacitors and inductors, which are found in elliptic

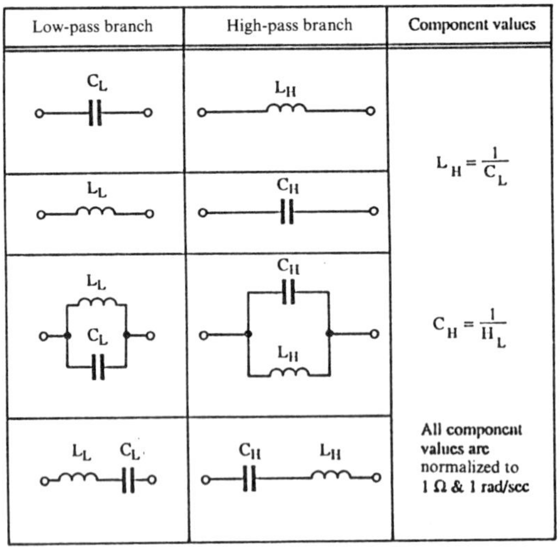

Low-pass branch	High-pass branch	Component values
C_L	L_H	$L_H = \dfrac{1}{C_L}$
L_L	C_H	
L_L C_L	C_H L_H	$C_H = \dfrac{1}{L_L}$
L_L C_L	C_H L_H	All component values are normalized to 1 Ω & 1 rad/sec

Figure 3.6 *Low-pass to high-pass branch transformations. The low-pass component values must be in their normalized format before being inverted.*

low-pass filters, are also shown and each component is simply transformed separately.

The results of applying these transformations to typical third-order low-pass filters are shown in Fig. 3.7. The two circuits shown are typical of the Butterworth, Chebyshev and Bessel low-pass filters described in Chapter 2. The top circuit shows the minimum inductor low-pass implementation which, when transformed, results in a minimum capacitor high-pass filter, whereas the bottom circuit shows the minimum capacitor low-pass circuit, resulting in a minimum inductor high-pass filter. The usefulness of the dual networks presented in Chapter 2 can now be seen: the implementation required for a normalized low-pass filter design can depend on whether the final use of the filter is as a denormalized low-pass filter or as a prototype for a frequency transformation.

The design procedure for high-pass filters can therefore be seen to consist of five steps:

1. normalization of the high-pass filtering requirement;
2. conversion of this requirement into the equivalent low-pass specification;

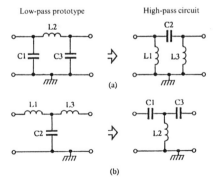

Figure 3.7 *Low-pass to high-pass transformation of non-elliptic-type filters showing:*
a) Minimum inductor low-pass prototype
b) Minimum capacitor low-pass prototype

3. selection of a low-pass prototype filter using the low-pass design information given in Chapter 2 which meets the equivalent low-pass specification;
4. transformation of this low-pass filter to a high-pass filter by replacing all capacitors by inductors and all inductors by capacitors, each component having a value of the reciprocal of the prototype component;
5. denormalization, or scaling, of this normalized high-pass filter to meet the original frequency and impedance specification.

As an illustration, an audio high-pass filter is required which must have a 3 dB cut-off frequency of 300 Hz and an attenuation of at least 40 dB at 100 Hz, increasing at lower frequencies. The source and termination impedances must be 1 kΩ and there should be no ripples in the passband.

Since the passband must contain no ripples and the 3 dB attentuation cut-off frequency is defined, a Butterworth filter is required. Normalizing the 300 Hz cut-off frequency to 1 rad/s, the frequency at which the stopband attenuation is specified, ω_s, is 0.333 rad/s, which gives 3 rad/s for the low-pass prototype specification. Reference to Fig. 2.9 or equation 2.5 gives a rounded order for the filter of 5. The normalized B05 filter data can therefore be extracted from Table 2.1, giving the two possible configurations shown in Fig. 3.8. Because these circuits are duals of each other, either will satisfy the high-pass filtering specification when transformed and scaled. Remembering that each low-pass capacitor will result in a high-pass inductor and vice versa, the minimum capacitor low-pass prototype is the best choice if, as is usually the case, a minimum inductor high-pass filter is desired. The circuit of Fig. 3.8 (b) therefore transforms to Fig. 3.9 (a) where each transformed component has a value of the reciprocal of the low-pass prototype value. Scaling the filter to 300 Hz, 1 kΩ, equation 2.14 gives a scaling factor for the capacitors of

$$\frac{1}{2 \times \pi \times 300 \times 1000} = 5.305 \times 10^{-7}$$

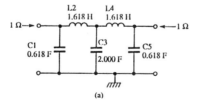

Figure 3.8 *The dual implementations of the Butterworth low-pass filters B05, selected as possible candidates for the low-pass to high-pass transformation*
a) Shows the minimum inductor implementation
b) Shows the minimum capacitor implementation

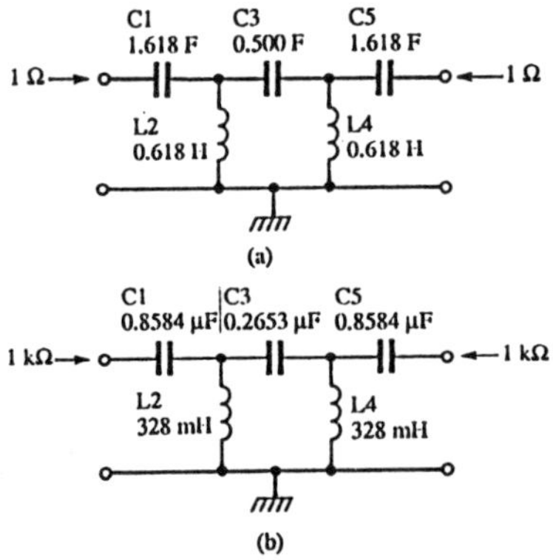

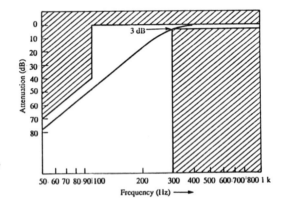

Figure 3.9 *The transformed high-pass filter, resulting in the minimum inductor implementation*
a) Shows the normalized component values
b) Shows the 300 Hz, 1 k Ω values

Figure 3.10 *Simulated amplitude response of the Butterworth high-pass filter shown in Fig. 3.9(b)*

For the inductors, equation 2.15 gives a scaling factor of

$$\frac{1000}{2 \times \pi \times 300} = 0.5305$$

Figure 3.9 (b) shows the final circuit with the scaled component values.

This circuit has been simulated assuming exact and ideal components and the results are plotted in Fig. 3.10: the high-pass filtering specification is shown as shading on this diagram. The 300 Hz cut-off frequency has been met exactly, and the 40 db attenuation at 100 Hz has been exceeded, about 47 dB being achieved due to the rounding of the filter order. Below 100 Hz the attentuation continues to increase, as specified, being about 78 dB at 50 Hz.

The band-pass filter response

Figure 3.11 shows the ideal band-pass amplitude response. The response has a passband positioned between lower and upper cut-off frequencies, which mark the transition frequencies between the lower stopband and the pass-

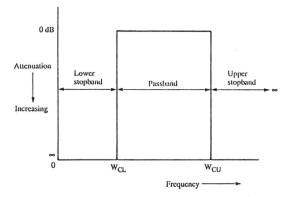

Figure 3.11 *The ideal band-pass filter amplitude response*

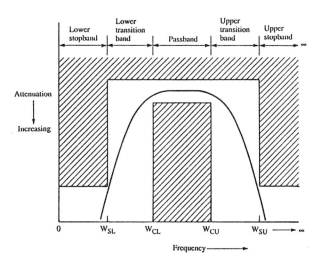

Figure 3.12 *A method of specifying a band-pass filtering amplitude requirement. The shading represents areas into which the response curve cannot enter*

band, and the passband and the upper stopband. A more reasonable specification for a band-pass filter is shown in Fig. 3.12. Lower and upper cut-off frequencies, ω_{cl} and ω_{cu}, as well as lower and upper stopband frequencies, ω_{sl} and ω_{su}, are specified, with reasonable frequency spans forming transition bands between the passband and stopband regions. As drawn, Fig. 3.12 shows a similar attenuation specified for the lower and upper stopbands, but this does not necessarily have to be the case, as will be illustrated later.

A simple band-pass filter

A simple band-pass filter which may be familiar is a shunt-connected parallel tuned circuit formed by a capacitor and an inductor, as shown in Fig. 3.13. The network is driven by a voltage source via a resistor and terminated by another resistor. Such an apparently simple circuit has a complex response depending not only on R_s and R_L, but also on the absolute values chosen for

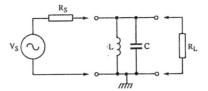

Figure 3.13 *A simple band-pass filter formed from a parallel combination of an inductor and a capacitor.*

C and L to resonate at a particular frequency, of which there are, of course, an infinite number. As higher values of resistor are used, the peak in the response at the resonant frequency becomes sharper. This sharpness can be quantified by finding the band-pass Q of the response which is given by

$$Q_{bp} = \frac{f_0}{BW_{3dB}} \tag{3.1}$$

where Q_{bp} is the band-pass Q,
       f_0 is the centre of frequency,
       BW_{3dB} is the 3 dB attenuation bandwith.

For a given set of C and L values, doubling the source and terminating resistor values has the effect of doubling the band-pass Q, giving a sharper peak to the response.

If the centre frequency of the simple band-pass filter response is f_0, it is related to the 3 dB cut-off frequencies by the relationship

$$f_0 = \sqrt{f_{cl} \times f_{cu}} \tag{3.2}$$

where f_{cl} is the lower cut-off (3 dB) frequency,
       f_{cu} is the upper cut-off (3 dB) frequency.

In general, f_0 is related to any two frequencies of equal attenuation by the relationship

$$f_0 = \sqrt{f_{xl} \times f_{xu}} \tag{3.3}$$

where: f_{xl} is the lower x dB attenuation frequency,
        f_{xu} is the upper x dB attenuation frequency.

In mathematical terms, f_0 is the geometric centre frequency of the response and the total response is symmetrical about f_0. For band-pass Q values of 10 or more, the geometric centre frequency can be approximated by the arithmetic centre frequency, given by

$$f_0 = \frac{f_{cl} + f_{cu}}{2} \tag{3.4}$$

where the symbols have the same meaning as in equation 3.2. Equations 3.2–3.4 can also be expressed in terms of angular frequency if required, by substituting ω for f in each equation.

If the 3 dB bandwith of a parallel tuned circuit is known, the attenuation A at any other bandwith can be determined from the equation:

$$A = 10 \log_{10}\left[1 + \left(\frac{BW_{xdB}}{BW_{3dB}} \right)^2 \right] dB \tag{3.5}$$

where BW_{3dB} is the dB attenuation bandwith,
BW_{xdB} is the bandwith at which the attenuation is desired.

The similarity between equation 3.5 and equation 2.4, the Butterworth low-pass filter attenuation equation with $n = 1$, can be seen. The single tuned circuit amplitude response is identical to a first-order Butterworth filter response. Away from resonance, the response tends towards $-6\,dB/octave$ below the resonant frequency, and $+6\,dB/octave$ above the resonant frequency. The cause of the $-6\,dB/octave$ roll-off rate below resonance is the high-pass action of the inductor; the low-pass action of the capacitor causes the $+6\,dB/octave$ roll-off above resonance. Away from resonance, the response of the total network can therefore be considered to be the sum of the individual low-pass and high-pass responses of the components. Although the filter contains two components, a capacitor and an inductor, it is still only a first-order band-pass filter since, at any frequency away from resonance, only one component affects the response significantly.

Equation 3.5 can be rearranged to enable the bandwith to be calculated at which a certain attenuation is achieved. This can be determined from:

$$BW_{xdB} = BW_{3dB} \sqrt{10^{A/10} - 1} \qquad (3.6)$$

where the symbols have the same meaning as in equation 3.5.

Where a simple band-pass response is required, for example at the front end of an amateur bands receiver, this parallel tuned circuit filter can be an ideal solution. The amateur bands all have a comparatively high ratio of centre frequency to bandwidth and so highly peaked band-pass filters are ideal. The UK 3.5 MHz amateur band, for example, has a bandwidth of 300 kHz and the geometric centre frequency is 3.647 MHz (very nearly equal to the arithmetic centre frequency of 3.65 MHz) giving a required band-pass Q of 12.16 so long as 3 dB of attenuation can be tolerated at the band edges. This is by no means an extreme example; the 18 MHz amateur band ideally requires a band-pass Q of approximately 180. To help achieve this optimum band-pass Q, the band-pass filter is often driven by transformer-coupled windings or taps on the inductor to raise the impedance level of the relatively low-impedance antennas used to a value which gives a high band-pass Q. Cascaded sets of LC band-pass filters are also used to increase the sharpness of the response. A set of filters suitable for the amateur bands below 30 MHz using pre-wound inductors is described in Chapter 6.

The low-pass to band-pass transformation

In the same way that a low-pass to high-pass transformation is available, a transformation can be applied to a low-pass filter to give a band-pass response. The transformation is shown in Fig. 3.14, where the low-pass prototype components have the subscript L and the transformed band-pass components have the subscript P. Each low-pass capacitor is resonated with a parallel inductor and each low-pass inductor is resonated with a series capacitor at the geometric centre frequency of the desired band-pass

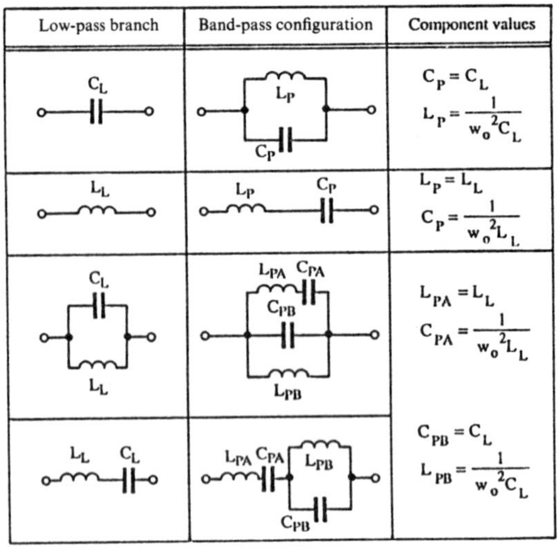

Low-pass branch	Band-pass configuration	Component values
C_L	L_P C_P	$C_P = C_L$ $L_P = \dfrac{1}{w_o^2 C_L}$
L_L	L_P C_P	$L_P = L_L$ $C_P = \dfrac{1}{w_o^2 L_L}$
C_L L_L	L_{PA} C_{PA} C_{PB} L_{PB}	$L_{PA} = L_L$ $C_{PA} = \dfrac{1}{w_o^2 L_L}$
L_L C_L	L_{PA} C_{PA} L_{PB} C_{PB}	$C_{PB} = C_L$ $L_{PB} = \dfrac{1}{w_o^2 C_L}$

Figure 3.14 *Low-pass to band-pass branch transformations*

response. Composite branches are transformed by treating each component separately.

The effect of applying the low-pass to band-pass transformation to typical third-order filters of Butterworth, Chebyshev or Bessel types is shown in Fig. 3.15. Since the transformation involves resonating each prototype capacitor with a parallel inductor and each prototype inductor with a series capacitor, there is no advantage in choosing a minimum inductor or minimum capacitor low-pass prototype, since each results in the same number of band-pass capacitors and inductors. The transformation results in a symmetrical amplitude response for the final filter and Fig. 3.16 shows such a symmetrical Butterworth band-pass response.

The choice of low-pass filter which will produce the required band-pass response when transformed is made by converting the band-pass requirement into an equivalent low-pass specification and designing the low-pass prototype to meet this specification. Table 3.1 shows the method of specifying a band-pass filter, with the equivalent low-pass specification. The

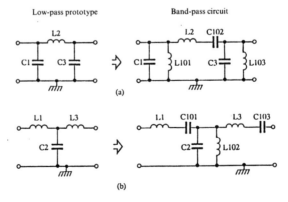

Figure 3.15 *Low-pass to band-pass transformation of non-elliptic-type filters showing:*
a) minimum inductor low-pass prototype
b) minimum capacitor low-pass prototype

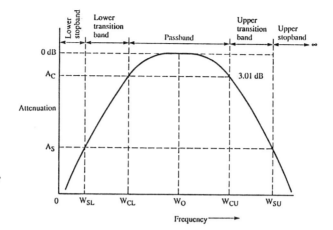

Figure 3.16 *The idealized Butterworth band-pass filter response. The response shown here is symmetrical about W_0, implying that:*
$$\omega_0{}^2 = \omega_{cl} \times \omega_{cu} = \omega_{sl} \times \omega_{su}$$

Table 3.1 *Comparison of a symmetrical band-pass specification with the equivalent low-pass specification*

		SYMMETRICAL BANDPASS SPECIFICATION	EQUIVALENT LOWPASS SPECIFICATION
FILTER APPROXIMATION		Butterworth, Chebyshev etc	Identical to bandpass specification
CENTRE FREQUENCY		w0 rads/sec or f0 Hz	No equivalent
PASSBAND RIPPLE		Ap	Ap
PASSBAND BANDWIDTH	BUTTERWORTH, BESSEL	BW 3dB	wc
	CHEBYSHEV, ELLIPTIC	BW ApdB	wp
STOPBAND BANDWIDTH		BW AsdB	ws
STOPBAND ATTENUATION		As	As
SOURCE AND TERMINATION IMPEDANCES		Z ohm	Z ohm

filter approximation, passband ripple, stopband attenuation, and source and termination impedances are identical for the band-pass and low-pass specifications. Since the low-pass response begins at 0 rad/s, the low-pass equivalent of, say, the band-pass 3 dB (or A_p) bandwith is from 0 to ω_c (or ω_p) rad/s, or simply ω_c (or ω_p) rad/s.

Unlike the low-pass to high-pass transformation which was carried out while the low-pass prototype was in its normalized form, the low-pass to band-pass transformation is most conveniently performed after the prototype has been scaled. The formula used to determine the value of a band-pass inductor, L_p, to resonate with a low-pass capacitor at f_0 Hz is

$$L_p = \frac{1}{4 \times \pi^2 \times f_0^2 \times C_L} \tag{3.7}$$

where f_0 is the geometric centre frequency,
  C_L is the low-pass capacitor value.

Similarly, the value of a band-pass capacitor C_p, can be calculated by

$$C_p = \frac{1}{4 \times \pi^2 \times f_0^2 \times L_L} \tag{3.8}$$

where f_0 is the geometric centre frequency,
  L_L is the low-pass inductor value.

The design procedure for symmetrical band-pass filters therefore consists of five steps:

1. conversion of the band-pass requirement into a geometrically symmetrical band-pass requirement;
2. conversion of the symmetrical band-pass requirement into an equivalent low-pass specification;
3. selection of a normalized low-pass prototype filter using the low-pass design information given in Chapter 2 which meets the equivalent low-pass specification;
4. denormalization, or scaling, of the low-pass prototype filter to the cut-off frequency of the equivalent low-pass specification and the required impedance level;
5. transformation of the scaled low-pass filter to a band-pass filter by resonating the low-pass components at the band-pass geometric centre frequency.

Although this procedure may at first seem complicated, an example will serve to illustrate its basic simplicity. A symmetrical band-pass filter is required for the front end of a receiver. The lower and upper cut-off frequencies are 1.5 MHz and 4 MHz, with a maximum passband ripple of 1 dB. The 40 dB bandwith of the filter must be not more than 5 MHz. The filter must operate between 50 Ω impedances and the stopband response must be monotonic.

Since 1 dB of passband ripple is allowed and a monotonic stopband response is required, a Chebyshev filter will be used. The geometric mean of the cut-off frequencies $f_0 = \sqrt{1.5 \times 4.0}$ MHz = 2.449 MHz. This is the geometric centre frequency. The equivalent low-pass filter must have a ripple cut-off frequency (when scaled) equal to the passband bandwith of the band-pass filter, which is (4–1.5) MHz = 2.5 MHz. The ratio of the stopband to passband bandwidth is 5 MHz/(4–1.5) MHz = 2, which is equivalent to $\omega_s = 2$ rad/s for the normalized low-pass prototype.

The equivalent low-pass specification is therefore

Type:	Chebyshev
passband ripple:	1 dB maximum
normalized ripple cut-off frequency:	1 rad/s
normalized source/termination impedance;	1 Ω
normalized start of stopband frequency:	2 rad/s
stopband attenuation;	40 dB
scaled ripple cut-off frequency:	2.5 MHz
scaled source/termination impedance:	50 Ω

Reference to the Chebyshev nomograph of Fig. 2.14 gives a required order very close to 5 and Table 2.8 contains the component values for the required low-pass prototype, C05 45. Figure 3.17 (a) shows the minimum inductor implementation of C05 45 and below it is shown the 2.5 MHz, 50 Ω scaled version. Capacitors have been multiplied by

$$\frac{1}{2 \times \pi \times 2.5 \times 10^6 \times 50} = 1.273 \times 10^{-9}$$

Inductors have been multiplied by

$$\frac{50}{2 \times \pi \times 2.5 \times 10^6} = 3.183 \times 10^{-6}$$

Figure 3.17 (c) shows the final band-pass filter, which now has the band-pass inductors and capacitors added to resonate with the low-pass components at 2.449 MHz. The band-pass components have the designations C_{101}, L_{101} and so on, to distinguish them from the low-pass components. Taking the calculation of L_{101}:

$$L_{101} = \frac{1}{4 \times \pi^2 \times (2.449 \times 10^6)^2 \times 2.718 \times 10^{-9}} = 1.554 \, \mu H$$

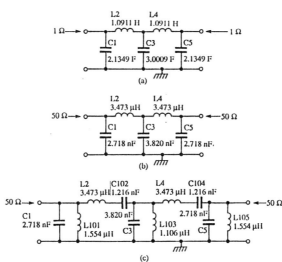

Figure 3.17 *The design procedure for a transformed band-pass filter showing:*
a) C05 45, the low-pass Chebyshev prototype
b) This filter scaled to 2.5 MHz, 50 Ω
c) The final band-pass design with a geometric centre frequency of 2.449 MHz

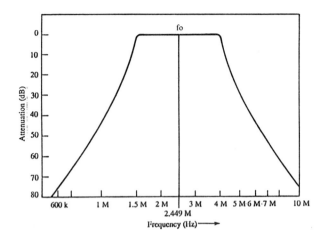

Figure 3.18 *Simulated amplitude response of the symmetrical bandpass filter shown in Fig. 3.1.7 (c)*

Simulation results of this band-pass filter are presented in Fig. 3.18. The 1 dB cut-off frequencies of 1.5 Mhz and 4 MHz have been met exactly and so has the passband ripple value of 1 dB, although this cannot be seen from the limited resolution of the diagram. The 40 dB attenuation frequencies are 1.06 MHz and 5.62 MHz, giving a 40 dB attenuation bandwidth of 4.56 MHz, narrower than required due to the rounding of the low-pass prototype order.

Asymmetrical band-pass filter design

So far, only symmetrical band-pass filters have been considered and two methods for their design described, namely parallel tuned circuits and the low-pass to band-pass transformation. A band-pass filter response might be specified as being asymmetrical having, for example, different roll-off requirements in the lower and upper stopbands or, in a more extreme example, requiring perhaps a Butterworth response in the lower stopband and an elliptic response in the upper stopband.

If a high-pass filter and a low-pass filter could be cascaded, and the filters were to maintain their individual responses when cascaded, then the overall response would be the sum of the filter responses. If buffering can be included between the cascaded filters they will be independent of each other and the total response will be predictable. Considerable savings will be made, however, if no buffering is required.

Computer simulations and practical experiments have shown that this aim can be achieved, excellent results being obtained with no intermediate buffering. In this arrangement, the high-pass filter relies on the low-pass filter to provide its termination impedance and the low-pass filter relies on the high-pass filter for its source impedance. So long as the cut-off frequencies of the two filters are sufficiently separated, say by one octave minimum, and if the filters are both designed for the same impedance level, each will present a sufficiently good match to the other for the overall response to be very nearly the sum of the individual responses. There is no requirement for the filters to be of the same approximation. This technique is usually considered only for comparatively wideband band-pass filters, but for many applications the consequences of designing much narrower cascaded band-pass filters are immaterial. Interaction between cascaded filters can be minimized by isolating the filters with constant-impedance attenuator networks,[1,2] the design of which is described in Chapter 6. Computer simulation of proposed designs allows their responses to be investigated, and judged suitable or not before any components are bought.

This technique is a very powerful method of designing comparatively wideband band-pass filters and a set of RF filters designed in this way, suitable for a general-coverage receiver, is described in Chapter 6.

The band-stop filter response

Figure 3.19 shows the ideal band-stop amplitude response. The response has a stopband positioned between lower and upper cut-off frequencies, which

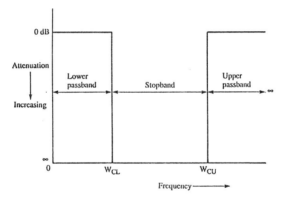

Figure 3.19 *The ideal band-stop filter amplitude response*

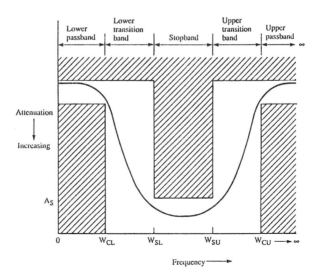

Figure 3.20 *A method of specifying a band-stop filtering amplitude requirement. The shading represents areas into which the response curve cannot enter*

mark the transitions between the lower passband and the stopband, and the stopband and the upper passband. A more reasonable specification for a band-stop filter is shown in Fig. 3.20. Lower and upper cut-off frequencies, ω_{cl} and ω_{cu}, as well as lower and upper stopband frequencies, ω_{sl} and ω_{su}, are specified, with reasonable transition bands defined. The lower cut-off frequency is now below the lower stopband frequency, and the upper cut-off frequency is above the upper stopband frequency, which contrasts with the band-pass filter response.

A simple band-stop filter

One simple band-stop filter is a series-connected parallel tuned circuit formed by a capacitor and an inductor, as shown in Fig. 3.21. The network is driven by a voltage source via a resistor and terminated by another resistor. At the resonant frequency of C and L, the tuned circuit represents an infinite impedance between the input and output and so a point of infinite attenuation should exist; this will only be true if ideal components are assumed for the capacitor and the inductor. Any losses in the filter components, which are inevitable in practice, will result in a finite value for the attenuation at resonance.

In the same way that a band-pass Q was calculated earlier for a band-pass filter, a band-stop Q can also be defined by

$$Q_{bs} = \frac{f_0}{BW_{3dB}}$$ (3.9)

where Q_{bs} is the band-stop Q,
          f_0 is the centre frequency,
          BW_{3dB} is the 3 dB attentuation bandwith.

A pair of equations are available to enable the attenuation at a given bandwidth, or the bandwidth for a given attenuation, to be calculated if the 3 dB bandwidth is known. These equations are

$$A = 10 \log_{10}\left[1 + \left(\frac{BW_{3dB}}{BW_{xdB}} \right)^2 \right] dB$$ (3.10)

and

$$BW_{xdB} = \frac{BW_{3dB}}{\sqrt{10^{A/10} - 1}}$$ (3.11)

where BW_{3dB} is the 3 dB attenuation bandwidth,
          BW_{xdB} is the bandwidth at which the attenuation is desired.

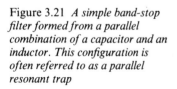

Figure 3.21 *A simple band-stop filter formed from a parallel combination of a capacitor and an inductor. This configuration is often referred to as a parallel resonant trap*

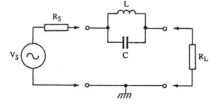

The high-pass to band-stop transformation

A transformation can be applied to a high-pass filter to produce a band-stop response. The transformation is shown in Fig. 3.22 where the high-pass components have the subscript H and the transformed band-stop components have the subscript S. Each high-pass capacitor is resonated with a parallel inductor and each high-pass inductor is resonated with a series capacitor at the geometric centre frequency of the desired band-stop response. Composite branches are transformed by transforming each component separately. Since the transformation involves resonating each high-pass capacitor with a parallel inductor, and each inductor with a series capacitor, there is no advantage in choosing a minimum inductor or minimum capacitor high-pass prototype, since each results in the same number of band-stop capacitors and inductors.

As in the low-pass to band-pass case, the result of the transformation is a symmetrical response for the final filter. Equations 3.2 and 3.3, relating the lower and upper cut-off frequencies and the lower and upper stopband frequencies to the geometric centre frequency, are also valid for the band-stop response. Again, the high-pass to band-stop transformation must be carried out after the high-pass filter has been scaled.

Clearly, a high-pass filter must be chosen which, when transformed, will give the required band-stop response. Since our technique for the design of high-pass filters relies on the transformation of low-pass prototypes, the band-stop requirement has to be traced back to a low-pass specification. Table 3.2 shows the method of specifying a band-stop filter, with the equivalent low-pass specification alongside.

The design procedure for symmetrical band-stop filters therefore consists of six steps

1. conversion of the band-stop requirement into a geometrically symmetrical band-stop requirement;

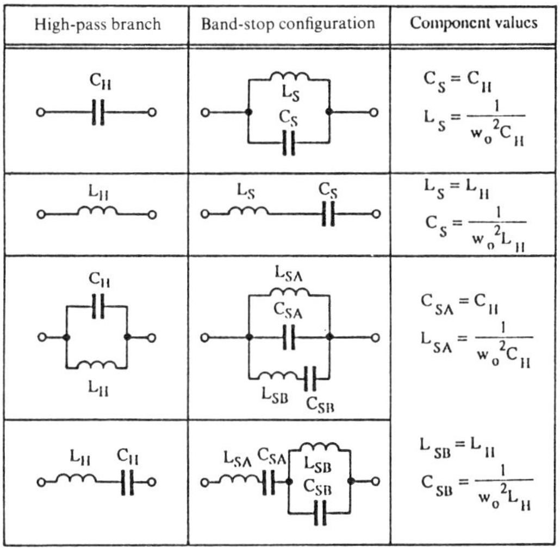

High-pass branch	Band-stop configuration	Component values
C_H	L_S C_S	$C_S = C_H$ $L_S = \dfrac{1}{w_o{}^2 C_H}$
L_H	L_S C_S	$L_S = L_H$ $C_S = \dfrac{1}{w_o{}^2 L_H}$
C_H L_H	L_{SA} C_{SA} L_{SB} C_{SB}	$C_{SA} = C_H$ $L_{SA} = \dfrac{1}{w_o{}^2 C_H}$
L_H C_H	L_{SA} C_{SA} L_{SB} C_{SB}	$L_{SB} = L_H$ $C_{SB} = \dfrac{1}{w_o{}^2 L_H}$

Figure 3.22 *High-pass to band-stop branch transformations*

Table 3.2 *Comparison of a symmetrical bandstop specification with the equivalent low-pass specification*

```
                                   SYMMETRICAL          EQUIVALENT
                                    BANDSTOP             LOWPASS
                                  SPECIFICATION        SPECIFICATION
----------------------------------------------------------------------
  FILTER APPROXIMATION            Butterworth,          Identical to
                                  Chebyshev etc    bandstop specification
----------------------------------------------------------------------
    CENTRE FREQUENCY              w0 rads/sec or        No equivalent
                                     f0 Hz
----------------------------------------------------------------------
    PASSBAND RIPPLE                    Ap                    Ap
----------------------------------------------------------------------
            | BUTTERWORTH,           BW 3dB                  wc
  CUT-OFF   | BESSEL
            |-----------------------------------------------------------
  BANDWIDTH | CHEBYSHEV,             BW ApdB                 wp
            | ELLIPTIC
----------------------------------------------------------------------
  STOPBAND BANDWIDTH                 BW AsdB                 ws
----------------------------------------------------------------------
  STOPBAND ATTENUATION                 As                    As
----------------------------------------------------------------------
  SOURCE AND TERMINATION             Z ohm                 Z ohm
         IMPEDANCES
----------------------------------------------------------------------
```

2. conversion of the symmetrical band-stop requirement into an equivalent low-pass specification;
3. selection of a normalized low-pass prototype filter using the low-pass design information given in Chapter 2 which meets the equivalent low-pass specification;
4. transformation of the normalized low-pass prototype filter into a normalized high-pass filter;
5. denormalization, or scaling, of the high-pass filter to the cut-off frequency of the equivalent low-pass requirement and the required impedance level;
6. transformation of the scaled high-pass filter to a band-stop filter by resonating the low-pass components at the band-stop geometric centre frequency.

An example will serve to illustrate the procedure. A Butterworth band-stop filter is required with 3 dB cut-off frequencies of 8 MHz and 12 MHz and it must achieve 50 dB attenuation at a bandwidth of 500 kHz. The filter must work between impedances of $300/\Omega$.

The geometric centre frequency $f_0 = \sqrt{8 \times 12}$ MHz $= 9.798$ mHz. The equivalent low-pass filter must have a 3 dB cut-off frequency (when scaled) equal to the 3 dB bandwidth of the band-stop filter, which is 4 MHz. The ratio of the 3 dB bandwidth to the stopband bandwidth is 4 MHz/500 kHz, which is equivalent to $\omega_s = 8$ rad/s for the normalized low-pass prototype. The equivalent low-pass specification is therefore

Type:	Butterworth
normalized 3 dB cut-off frequency:	1 rad/s
normalized source/termination impedance:	1Ω

normalized start of stopband frequency: 8 rad/s
stopband attenuation: 50 dB
scaled cut-off frequency: 4 MHz
scaled source/termination impedance: 300 Ω

Equation 2.5 gives a required order of 2.768 for the low-pass prototype, which is rounded to 3. The component values for B03 are extracted from Table 2.1 and Fig. 3.23 (a) shows its circuit diagram with these normalized component values. Figure 3.23 (b) shows the filter converted into the normalized high-pass filter, and Fig. 3.23 (c) shows the component values scaled to 4 MHz, 300 Ω. Finally, Fig. 3.23 (d) shows the required band-stop filter with

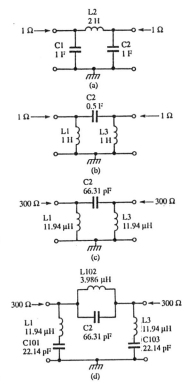

Figure 3.23 *The design procedure for a transformed band-stop filter showing:*
a) B03, the normalized low-pass prototype
b) The transformed normalized high-pass filter
c) The high-pass filter scaled to 4 MHz, 300 Ω
d) The final 9.798 MHz centre frequency, 300 Ω band-stop design

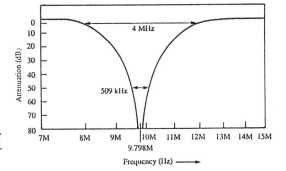

Figure 3.24 *Simulated amplitude response of the symmetrical band-stop filter shown in Fig. 3.23 (d)*

the extra components added to resonate the high-pass components at 9.798 MHz.

Figure 3.24 shows the simulated response of the filter. The 4 MHz bandwidth specification has been met exactly, and the 50 dB attenuation bandwidth is 509 kHz, slightly wider than specified because of the rounding of the low-pass prototype filter order.

Asymetrical band-stop filters

Earlier in this chapter the technqiue of cascading low-pass and high-pass filters to produce asymetrical band-pass filters was described. In a similar manner, asymmetrical band-stop filters can be produced by connecting low-pass and high-pass filters in parallel and connecting the input and output terminals of each filter together.

For the technique to be valid, each filter must have a high input and output impedance in the passband of the other filter. This restriction makes this method of design difficult and undesirable, and the transformation method is preferable. In practice, a requirement for an asymmetrical band-stop filter is unlikely to arise and so this restriction will not be a great limitation in the overall filter design technique.

Summary and conclusions

The simplest high-pass filter was seen to be a single, series-connected capacitor and, in its commonest use as a DC blocking component, its filtering properties in association with the surrounding circuit impedances must be taken into account if undesired effects are to be avoided. The response of this simple high-pass filter was the mirror image of the simple low-pass filter, indicating a strong relationship between the two responses.

A high-pass filter can be obtained from a normalized low-pass prototype by transforming the original capacitors into inductors, the inductors into capacitors, and taking the reciprocal of the original values of the components. The resulting normalized high-pass filter is then scaled in exactly the same way as a low-pass filter to work at the intended cut-off frequency and impedance level. Because the transformation results in prototype capacitors becoming inductors and vice versa, it is important to select the optimum low-pass prototype dual if a particular configuration of high-pass filter, for example the minimum inductor implementation, is required.

A shunt-connected parallel tuned circuit was quoted as an example of a simple band-pass filter. The sharpness of the peak obtained was seen to depend on the value of source and termination resistors, increasing as the resistors were raised in value. A method of quantifying this sharpness by defining the band-pass Q of the response is also relevant to all band-pass filters, not just the simple example shown.

Two methods of designing more complex band-pass filters were described:

1. transformation of a low-pass filter by resonating each low-pass capacitor with a parallel inductor and each low-pass inductor with a series capacitor

at the geometric centre frequency, resulting in a symmetrical band-pass response;

2. cascading a low-pass and a high-pass filter having the same impedances and fairly widely separated cut-off frequencies, allowing the implementation of asymmetrical responses if required.

A series-connected parallel tuned circuit was shown as an example of a simple band-stop filter. At the resonant frequency of the tuned circuit, and assuming perfect, loss-free components, the circuit has infinite attenuation. Any imperfections in the components used reduces this attenuation to some finite level. As was found with the simple band-pass filter, the sharpness of the rejection notch in the simple band-stop response is dependent on the source and terminating resistor values.

Again two methods are available for the design of band-stop filters:

1. transformation of a high-pass filter, which itself has to be produced by a low-pass to high-pass transformation, to a band-stop filter by resonating each high-pass capacitor with a parallel inductor and each high-pass inductor with a series capacitor at the geometric centre frequency, resulting in a symmetrical band-stop response;

2. connecting a low-pass and a high-pass filter in parallel, commoning together the inputs and outputs, though this is not as likely to result in success as the cascading method for band-pass design.

References

1. A.B. Williams, *Electronic Filter Design Handbook*, 1981. McGraw-Hill, Table 5–1.
2. G.R. Jessop, *Radio Data Reference Book*, 5th edition, 1985. RSGB, Part 5, p. 151.

4   Active low-pass filters

As the name implies, active filters incorporate elements which can give gain, such as transisors, or more commonly nowadays, operational amplifiers. Because active filters are used extensively in electronics, no book covering filters would be complete without a treatment of the subject. Many of the concepts described in the previous chapters are relevant to active filters: normalization, scaling, filter approximations and transformations are all valid and the knowledge gained from studying passive filters is an useful base on which to build familiarity with their active counterparts.

The main impetus behind the development of active filters was the elimination of inductors, allowing filter implementations which use only resistors, capacitors and the active elements themselves. Inductors are now considered to be bulky, expensive and difficult to manufacture and of potentially low Q, giving degraded performance. Although the elimination of inductors from filters is a significant advance, active filters should not be seen as the answer to all filtering requirements; op-amps produce noise, consume power, have a limited dynamic range and a comparatively low upper-frequency limit. Modern op-amps are designed to reduce these limitations as much as possible and low-pass filters with cut-off frequencies up to several hundred kHz are possible using reasonably priced op-amps. There are few applications where active filters with such high cut-off frequencies are required and they are usually seen working at audio frequencies. In many applications, passive filters using inductors can still give the most cost-effective and compact solution, even at audio frequencies, and of course at radio frequencies they are essential.

With passive filters, the number of possible circuit implementations of a given response is fairly small: in the case of low-pass filters only two implementations, the duals, were identified for each approximation in Chapter 2. With active filters, however, many implementations have been devised over the years, each intended to optimize operation for a particular application. In any treatment of active filters, only a very few of these possibilities can be shown, and this book is no exception. The reader is bound to come across circuits which claim to be active filters (and most probably are) but which cannot readily be identified as such. Here again is a case for having a circuit simulator available to allow verification of the circuit and investigation into the effects of modifying it, if desired.

Many books describe active filters in terms of the roots in the complex plane of the equations which define the filter response. If the reader has not had the benefit of an advanced mathematical education, this can destroy any hope of understanding and using these filters. In this chapter the approach will be to describe responses in terms of damping and frequency variables which control responses, in ways which are easier to understand than the complex-roots approach. Only towards the end of the chapter will complex roots be mentioned again, when a method of converting these roots, of which there are many published catalogues, into the damping and frequency format will be explained.

Reference 1 is one fairly cheap book which might be found useful reading on active filters, whereas reference 2 is rather more expensive, but contains a great deal more information.

Operational amplifier circuits

Before active filter configurations using op-amps are considered, it is useful to look at some basic op-amp circuits. The derivations of the equations which define, for example, the gain of these circuits are not included here and reference should be made to one of many books available on the subject[3,4,5,6]. Five simple configurations are described in this section.

- The voltage follower is a unity-gain, high input-impedance, low output-impedance non-inverting amplifier.
- The non-inverting voltage amplifier is a high input-impedance, low output-impedance amplifier having a gain of 1 or more.
- The inverting amplifier is a moderate input-impedance, low output impedance amplifier providing any reasonable value of gain.
- The summing block is an amplifier having several inputs, a moderate input impedance, a low output impedance and settable gains for each input.
- The integrator is an inverting, frequency-dependent amplifier.

Figure 4.1 shows the op-amp voltage follower. The input signal is fed into the non-inverting input and the high gain of the op-amp forces the differences between the two inputs to be effectively zero. Since the inverting input is connected to the output, the output follows the input signal. Note that R_1 is not part of the op-amp circuit: it represents the source impedance of the input voltage source, V_s. Resistance R_2 does not necessarily have to be included;

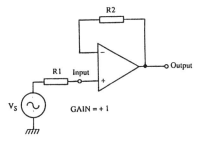

Figure 4.1 *The op-amp voltage follower*

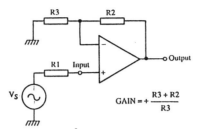

Figure 4.2 *The non-inverting amplifier with gain*

the output can be connected directly to the inverting input, but its inclusion means that the output offset can be minimized by making its value identical to the impedance to earth seen by the non-inverting input. The advantage of this configuration is that it presents a very small load to the input signal and is capable of driving a relatively low-impedance load. It is the op-amp equivalent of the emitter follower, but without the disadvantage of the less than unity voltage gain. Note that although this circuit gives no voltage gain, its power gain is considerable, because the output impedance is much lower than the input impedance.

Figure 4.2 shows the non-inverting amplifier with gain. An extra resistor R_3, has been added to the previous configuration, between the inverting input and earth. This forms a potential divider chain in association with R_2 which results in only a proportion of the output being fed back to the inverting input. Since the op-amp is always trying to force the difference between its inputs to zero, the output must go to a higher voltage than in the circuit of Fig. 4.1 for its potted-down version to be equal to the input signal. Hence, the stage has voltage gain. The voltage gain of the stage is given by:

$$\text{gain} = + \frac{R_3 + R_2}{R_3} \tag{4.1}$$

This equation tell us two things of interest: first, since R_2 and R_3 are always positive, the gain is also positive, meaning that the circuit is non-inverting, and secondly, the gain is always greater than 1 since the sum of R_3 and R_2 must be greater than R_3 alone. As in the voltage follower circuit, the gain is independent of the source impedance, R_1, of the input signal.

If a more versatile circuit which can give attenuation as well as gain is required, the inverting amplifier shown in Fig. 4.3 can be used. Here the voltage gain is given by:

$$\text{gain} = - \frac{R_2}{R_1} \tag{4.2}$$

The gain is always negative, implying that the circuit is inverting, and its magnitude can be fractional, unity or greater than 1.

At its inverting input the op-amp presents an extremely low impedance to earth to AC signals, hence the description of this input as a 'virtual earth'. The input impedance seen by the input signal, V_s, is therefore the value of R_1. Therefore, the absolute value of R_1 is chosen to present the desired impedance to the input signal (not necessarily simply as high as possible, since R_1

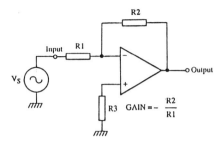

Figure 4.3 *The inverting amplifier*

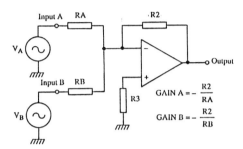

Figure 4.4 *The two input inverting amplifier*

can be chosen to correctly terminate a passive filter output and the ratio of R_2 to R_1 chosen to give the correct voltage again. A variable gain circuit can be obtained by replacing R_1 or R_2 by a variable resistor. If it is important to keep the input impedance constant, then R_2 should be the component which is made variable. To minimize output-offset errors, R_3 should be chosen to be approximately equal to the parallel combination of R_1 and R_2, though a compromise value must be used if a variable-gain circuit is being used.

It is sometimes useful to be able to add input signals and the previous circuit can be adapted into the summing block shown in Fig. 4.4. Two input voltage sources are shown, though more can be added, each fed through a separate input resistor. The gain for each input is given by:

$$\text{gain A} = -\frac{R_2}{R_A} \tag{4.3}$$

$$\text{gain B} = -\frac{R_2}{R_B} \tag{4.4}$$

The gains for each input are therefore independent and can be set to different values, so long as a compromise value for R_2 can be found. Inputs are inverted and the input impedance for each source is the value of its input resistor.

A more generalized summing block configuration is shown in Fig. 4.5. There can be several voltage sources driving both the inverting and the non-inverting inputs via resistors: Fig. 4.5 shows just two on the inverting input and one on the non-inverting input.

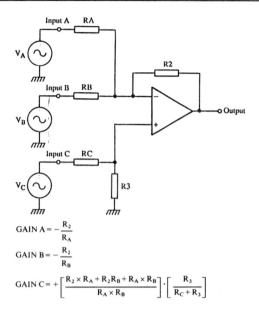

$$\text{GAIN A} = -\frac{R_2}{R_A}$$

$$\text{GAIN B} = -\frac{R_2}{R_B}$$

$$\text{GAIN C} = +\left[\frac{R_2 \times R_A + R_2 R_B + R_A \times R_B}{R_A \times R_B}\right] \cdot \left[\frac{R_3}{R_C + R_3}\right]$$

Figure 4.5 *The general purpose summing block*

The gain for input signals V_A and V_B are given in equations 4.3 and 4.4, and for V_C, the gain is given by

$$\text{gain C} = +\left[\frac{R_2.R_A + R_2.R_B + R_A.R_B}{R_A.R_B}\right] \cdot \left[\frac{R_3}{R_C + R_3}\right] \qquad (4.5)$$

The gain for the non-inverting input is therefore not independent of the gains for the inverting inputs, and always has a value equal to or greater than 1. Although this circuit may at first seem strange, and the expression for the non-inverting input gain complicated, it will be seen later that this is a useful building block for some types of active filters.

All the circuits described so far are, in theory at least, independent of the frequency of the input waveforms. If the feedback resistor of the circuit in Fig. 4.3 is replaced by a capacitor, the configuration shown in Fig. 4.6 is obtained. This is the op-amp integrator, so called because the capacitor causes the circuit to generate an output which represents the 'area under the curve' of the input waveform. Square-wave inputs are converted to triangular-wave outputs but, of more interest to us here, sine-wave inputs suffer a phase shift at the output and a gain which is frequency-dependent

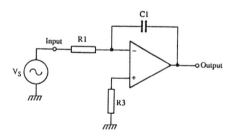

Figure 4.6 *The operational amplifier integrator circuit*

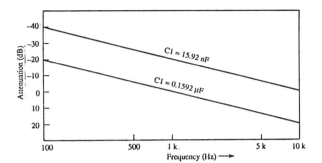

Figure 4.7 *Amplitude response of the op-amp integrator circuit of Fig. 4.6 R_1 has been set equal to 1 kΩ, and the response is plotted for two values of C_1: 0.1592 μF and 15.92 nF*

because of the variation with frequency of the reactance of the feedback capacitor. If, for example, the input resistor R_1 is 1 KΩ and the feedback capacitor C_1 is 0.1592 μF, the phase shift at 1 kHz (that is, $1/2\pi R_1.C_1$ Hz), is 90° ($\pi/2$ rad) and the gain is 1. The amplitude response of this circuit for two values of C_1 is shown in Fig. 4.7. Since the circuit contains one capacitor, we should expect a first-order response and this is apparent from Fig. 4.7, showing a roll-off of 6 dB/octave or 20 dB/decade. The effect of varying C_1, is to shift the response up or down the attenuation axis, while the roll-off rate is constant. The circuit by itself has no obvious cut-off frequency, but it will be seen later to be useful in some types of second-order filter sections.

The first-order active low-pass section

One first-order section was shown in Fig. 4.6 and is an inverting configuration. There are several disadvantages with this configuration which restrict its use: firstly, the gain at DC is theoretically infinite, because the feedback network has infinite reactance at zero frequency, and secondly, the gain begins to roll-off at 6 dB/octave immediately above DC. A better first-order section is shown in Fig. 4.8 (a), consisting simply of an RC network, R_1 and C_1, buffered by a non-inverting amplifier stage. The filtering action is due entirely to R_1 and C_1 (as was shown early in Chapter 2) and the op-amp serves two purposes: it presents a high impedance to the RC network, and it provides a low impedance drive to any subsequent stage. The circuit of Fig. 4.8 (a) is of course simply the op-amp voltage follower, with a resistor and capacitor added to give the first-order roll-off. As such, it has a gain at DC of 1. If a voltage gain of greater than 1 is required, the circuit of Fig. 4.8 (b) can be used. This is the non-inverting amplifier with gain, again with a capacitor added to turn it into a filter.

Component values shown in Fig. 4.8 are normalized to 1 rad/s cut-off (3 dB attenuation) frequency and 1 Ω input impedance. If the gain of the circuit in Fig. 4.8 (b) at DC is K: and R_3 has the value of 1 Ω, R_2 must be made equal to K $-$ 1. If, for example, a DC gain of 4 (12 dB) is required, the normalized value of R_2 must be 4 $-$ 1 $=$ 3 Ω. Figure 4.9 shows these two first-order circuits scaled to 1 kHz cut-off frequency and 1 kΩ input impedance.

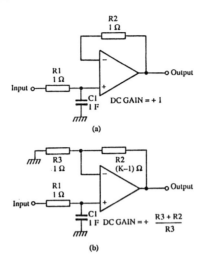

Figure 4.8 *Simple normalized first order low-pass active filter sections:*
a) Has a DC gain value of 1
b) Has a DC gain of $\dfrac{R_3 + R_2}{R_3}$

As in the passive filter case, equation 2.14 is used to scale the capacitor value, giving a new value for C_1 of

$$C_1 = \frac{1}{2 \times \pi \times 1000 \times 10^3} = 0.1592\mu F$$

In the circuit of Fig. 4.9 (b), the equal values of R_2 and R_3 give a DC gain of 2. At the cut-off frequency, the gain will be 3 dB down on its DC value giving a gain of $0.707 \times 2 = 1.414$ (3 dB) at 1 kHz. Since the filter exhibits a first-order response, the gain will roll-off at 6 dB/octave beyond about twice the cut-off frequency. Figure 4.10 shows the amplitude response of the circuits of Fig. 4.9.

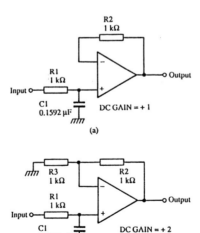

Figure 4.9 *First order low-pass sections scaled to 1 kHz, 1 kΩ:*
a) Has a DC gain of 1 (0 dB)
b) Has a DC gain of 2 (+6 dB)

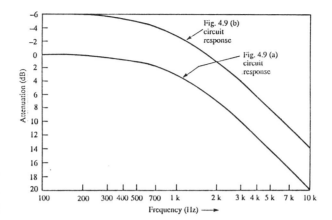

Figure 4.10 *Amplitude response of the first order low-pass active sections of Figs. 4.9(a) and (b). The upper curve is a replica of the lower curve but shifted up by 6 dB.*

Another first-order low-pass section, which is a variation on the basic integrator described earlier, is shown in Fig. 4.11. Here the feedback network is not simply a capacitor, but consists of a parallel combination of a capacitor and a resistor. At low frequencies, the capacitor has a high value of reactance and the resistor largely determines the gain of the circuit. As frequency increases, the reactance of the capacitor becomes smaller and so begins to effect, and eventually to dominate, the expression for the gain of the stage. The circuit is useful because it allows the cut-off frequency of the stage to be controlled, which was not possible with the simple integrator, and it also allows first-order sections with attenuation to be implemented, which is not possible with the circuits of Fig. 4.8.

At DC, the gain of the stage is given by equation 4.2, and the 3 dB attenuation (with respect to the DC gain) frequency is achieved when the reactance of the capacitor equals the feedback resistor value. The angular cut-off frequency, ω_c, is therefore given by

$$\omega_c = \frac{1}{R_2.C_1} \text{ rad/s} \tag{4.6}$$

or in more familiar terms

$$f_c = \frac{1}{2\pi R_2.C_1} \text{ Hz} \tag{4.7}$$

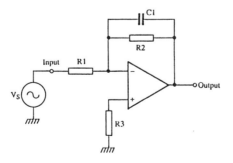

Figure 4.11 *The op-amp integrator with a resistor added to the feedback network to give better control of the frequency response*

The Sallen and Key second-order active low-pass section

Figure 4.12 shows a normalized second-order low-pass filter section, devised by Sallen and Key, by which name it is often known. Since the circuit is based on the non-inverting voltage follower circuit of Fig. 4.1, we would expect it to have a voltage gain of $+1$ at DC where the capacitors are effectively open circuits. Two frequency-dependent elements have been added, both capacitors, one directly on the non-inverting input of the op-amp and the other feeding back a proportion of the output waveform to the junction of the two input resistors.

As was seen in Chapter 2, a second-order filter section (such as the simple LC network shown in Fig. 2.5) can exhibit a variety of responses depending on the circuit Q designed into the section. In active circuits, the damping factor d which is the inverse of Q, is often used, and is equally significant in the performance of the filter. In Fig. 4.12 (a), d can be seen included in the expression for the values of the two capacitors. Before investigating the effect of various values of d, we will scale the component values to 1 kHz, 1 kΩ to work with more familiar values. The resistors are simply multiplied by 10^3 and the capacitors are multiplied by

$$\frac{1}{2 \times \pi \times 1000 \times 10^3} = 1.592 \times 10^{-7}$$

Figure 4.12 (b) shows the resulting component values. Remember that the value of the feedback resistor does not effect the gain of the stage, which is fixed at $+1$ at DC. Table 4.1 shows the values of C_1 and C_2 calculated for 5 values of d, and Fig. 4.13 illustrates how the amplitude response of the scaled filter changes with different values of d. Successively lower values of d, or higher values of Q, give a greater peak to the response and a faster initial roll-off rate.

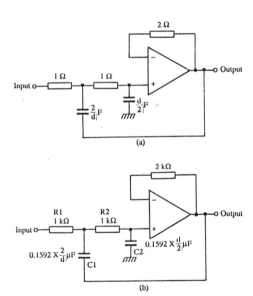

Figure 4.12 *The unity gain second order, Sallen and Key low-pass active section:*
a) normalized to 1 rad/sec, 1 Ω
b) scaled to 1 kHz, 1 kΩ

Table 4.1 *Values of d and corresponding values of C_1 and C_2 for the Sallen and Key circuit of Figure 4.12*

d	C1	C2
0.766	0.4157uF	60.97nF
0.886	0.3594uF	70.53nF
1.045	0.3049uF	83.18nF
1.414	0.2252uF	112.6nF
1.732	0.1840uF	137.7nF

When $d = 1.414$, the resulting response is the maximally flat Butterworth response, having an attenuation of 3 dB at 1 kHz. When $d = 1.045$, 0.886 and 0.766, second-order Chebyshev responses are obtained, having passband ripple values of 1 dB, 2 dB and 3 dB respectively. Note however, that the frequency to which the filters were scaled, 1 kHz, does not correspond to the frequency where the Chebyshev responses pass through the passband ripple value. The frequency at which the peak occurs (if there is one) and the frequency at which the attenuation is 0 dB again vary with d. Finally, when $d = 1.732$, the Bessel response is obtained, having a rather poor initial roll-off but a linear phase response. The ultimate roll-off rate for all d values is the same, at 12 dB/octave, which is standard for all second-order networks.

For responses with peaks, the normalized angular frequency, ω_{peak} at which the peak occurs is given by

$$\omega_{\text{peak}} = \sqrt{1 - \frac{d^2}{2}} \tag{4.8}$$

where d is the damping factor.

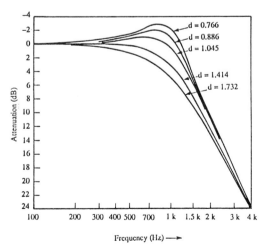

Figure 4.13 *Amplitude response of the unity gain, second order low-pass active section for various values of d. The circuit has been scaled to 1 kHz, 1 k Ω*

It can be seen that a value of ω_{peak} only exists for values of $d^2 < 2$, that is $d < 1.414$, and this represents the boundary value between the Butterworth and Chebyshev approximations. The amplitude of the peak, A_{peak} is given by

$$A_{peak} = 20 \log_{10} \left[\frac{d\sqrt{4-d^2}}{2} \right] dB \tag{4.9}$$

where d is the damping factor.

It would be useful to be able to move the response obtained from a second-order section up and down the frequency axis without affecting the value of d. This would allow the frequency at which the response passes through the 0 dB level to be made equal to 1 rad/s, so that what we have previously understood as the cut-off frequency for a normalized response can be set. This can be achieved by pre-scaling the capacitor values in the section by a factor ω_0. Lowering the values of the capacitors will increase the frequency at which the response reaches a particular attenuation, whereas increasing the values will lower this frequency. Therefore, the original capacitor values must be divided by ω_0 to give the pre-scaled values. The value of a pre-scaled capacitor is therefore given by

$$C_{pre} = C \times \frac{1}{\omega_0} \tag{4.10}$$

where C_{pre} is the pre-scaled capacitor value,
C is the original capacitor value,
ω_0 is the frequency scaling factor.

There are many variations on the basic Sallen and Key circuit, each optimized for a particular application having different gain, being inverting or non-inverting, and having certain component values equal. One particularly useful configuration is where the two capacitors are equal in value. This is shown in Fig. 4.14, in both its normalized form and also scaled to 1 kHz,

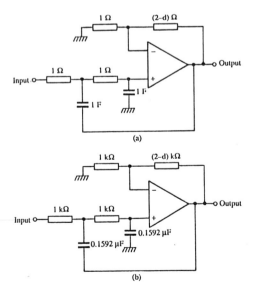

Figure 4.14 *The equal component value, second order, Sallen and Key low-pass active section:*
a) normalized to 1 rad/sec, 1 Ω
b) scaled to 1 kHz, 1 k Ω
The voltage gain of this configuration is 3–d

1 kΩ. The gain of this circuit is set at $3 - d$ and cannot be altered, which means that adjustment may have to be made elsewhere in the system to compensate for this gain if it is critical.

Butterworth low-pass active filter design

So far, we have considered first and second-order sections and seen that first-order sections can have the cut-off frequency set to any desired value, whereas second-order sections can have the damping factor d and ω_0 varied. With passive filters, design methods were presented which enable the order of the filter to range up to any value. The method adopted here for the design of active filters is to cascade first and second-order sections until the desired complexity is reached. This method of cascading can be extended to build up · filters of any order. What we need is a method of selecting the cut-off frequency for the first-order section (if the order of the filter is odd), and d and ω_0 for each of the second-order sections, so that the correct overall response is obtained.

In the same way that catalogues of normalized component values are available for passive filters, values of d and ω_0 can be tabulated for active filters. Table 4.2 is a catalogue for the Butterworth approximation for $n = 2$ to 10. For all odd-order filters, the values of d and ω_0 are constant for the first-order section, being equal to 2 and 1 respectively. For the second-order sections, only the value of d varies, as ω_0 is equal to 1 for all orders. This table completely describes these filters for all applications, since there is no added complexity of unequal terminations as there was in the passive case.

The design procedure will be explained by an example: an active Butterworth low-pass filter is required with a cut-off frequency of 4 kHz and it must achieve an attenuation of 30 dB with respect to its DC gain value by 8 kHz. The gain at DC must be 20 dB.

The first part of the design procedure is exactly the same as for a passive filter. Normalizing the cut-off frequency to 1 rad/s, we obtain the value of $\omega_s = 2$ rad/s for $A_s = 30$ dB. Applying equation 2.5, we obtain a required order of 4.98, which can also be seen from Fig. 2.9. A fifth-order filter is therefore required. Table 4.2 gives the values of d for the two second-order sections required, which will be preceded by a first-order section, giving the total order of 5 required. The DC gain requirement of 20 dB will be implemented in the first-order section, using the circuit of Fig. 4.8 (b) which allows the use of unity-gain Sallen and Key second-order sections as shown in Fig. 4.12 (a).

Generally speaking, it is best to cascade the sections with the most highly damped (lowest-Q) section first, putting the remaining sections in order of decreasing d. For this example, therefore, the first-order section is first ($d = 2$), followed by the $d = 1.618$ second-order section and finally the $d = 0.618$ second-order section, as shown in Fig. 4.15. The upper diagram is the filter with normalized component values. Remembering that the gain of the first-order section is given by $(R_3 + R_2)/R_3$, with R_2, with $R_2 = 9 \, \Omega$ and $R_3 = 1 \, \Omega$, a gain of 10 (20 dB) is obtained to meet the requirement.

Table 4.2 *Butterworth* d *and* ω_0 *values*

FILTER	ORDER	d	w0
B02	02	1.4142	1.0000
B03	03	1.0000	1.0000
		2.0000	1.0000
B04	04	0.7654	1.0000
		1.8478	1.0000
B05	05	0.6180	1.0000
		1.6180	1.0000
		2.0000	1.0000
B06	06	0.5175	1.0000
		1.4142	1.0000
		1.9319	1.0000
B07	07	0.4450	1.0000
		1.2470	1.0000
		1.8019	1.0000
		2.0000	1.0000
B08	08	0.3902	1.0000
		1.1111	1.0000
		1.6629	1.0000
		1.9616	1.0000
B09	09	0.3473	1.0000
		1.0000	1.0000
		1.5321	1.0000
		1.8794	1.0000
		2.0000	1.0000
B10	10	0.3129	1.0000
		0.9080	1.0000
		1.4142	1.0000
		1.7820	1.0000
		1.9754	1.0000

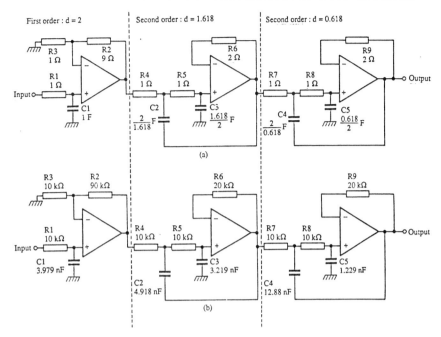

Figure 4.15 *Circuit diagrams of the 5th order Butterworth low-pass active filter used as an example*
a) has the normalized component values
b) has the 4 kHz, 10 k Ω component values
The DC gain of both these circuits is 10 (29 dB)

Before the filter can be scaled to its final cut-off frequency, the impedance level must be chosen to allow the resistor values to be set. With active filters, there is no requirement for the impedance level to be constant throughout a particular filter: each section can have a different impedance level if it helps to give more reasonable component values, but within a section only one impedance level can be used. In this example, we will set the impedance level to 10 k Ω and calculate the capacitor values accordingly. To scale the capacitors to 4 kHz, 10 k Ω, each capacitor must be multiplied by

$$\frac{1}{2 \times \pi \times 4000 \times 10^4} = 3.979 \times 10^{-9}$$

The 4 kHz, 10 k Ω value for C_1 therefore becomes 3.979 nF (since its normalized value is 1 F), and for C_2

$$C_2 = \frac{2}{1.618} \times 3.979 \times 10^{-9} = 4.918 \text{ nF}$$

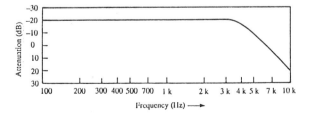

Figure 4.16 *Amplitude response of the 5th order Butterworth low-pass active filter shown in Fig. 4.15(a)*

The final scaled filter is shown in Fig. 4.15 (b), and the simulated amplitude response for this filter is shown in Fig. 4.16. The low-frequency gain of 20 dB is met exactly (since the vertical axis represents attenuation a gain is shown with a negative value) and the gain at 4 kHz is 3 dB less than at DC, meeting the classical Butterworth cut-off frequency definition. At 8 kHz the response is very close to being 30 dB down on the DC value. This would be expected because the theoretical order of the filter (4.98) was very close to the integer value implemented. The filter therefore meets the specification closely.

Chebyshev low-pass active filter design

When designing Butterworth active low-pass filters, it was necessary only to determine the value of d for each section, since ω_0 was the same for all the sections, at 1 rad/s. With Chebyshev filters, however, ω_0 must be defined for each section, so that the peaks in the individual amplitude responses of the second-order sections occur at the correct frequencies to produce the desired overall response. As with passive filters, we would expect a single table of d and ω_0 values to be inadequate to design a range of active Chebyshev filters, different values of pass-band ripple requiring a different set of d and ω_0 values for each section.

Tables 4.3–4.9 give the values of d and ω_0 for Chebyshev filters of orders from 2 to 10 for the same values of pass-band ripple as were presented for passive filters. The method of obtaining the values of d and ω_0 from a filter specification is shown in Chapter 7, along with a BASIC program which will perform the calculations for any value of pass-band ripple. Alternatively, reference 7 shows the Chebyshev pole locations for several values of pass-band ripple, and the method of converting these into d and ω_0 values is shown later in this chapter.

Let us say that a third-order, 1 dB pass-band ripple Chebyshev low-pass filter with a ripple cut-off frequency of 2.5 kHz is required. How is the data contained in the tables turned into the final filter design?

Table 4.9 contains the values of d and ω_0 for the 1 dB ripple filters. Making use of a first-order section cascaded with a unity-gain Sallen and Key second-order section, the normalized circuit shown in Fig. 4.17 (a) is obtained. The values of d and ω_0 have been included into the expressions for the capacitor values. The normalized value for C_1 is given by

$$C_1 = \frac{1}{d} = \frac{1}{0.4942} = 2.0235 \, \text{F}$$

Similarly, for C_2

$$C_2 = \frac{2}{d \times \omega_0} = \frac{2}{0.4956 \times 0.9971} = 4.0472 \, \text{F}$$

Figure 4.17 (b) shows the components scaled to 2.5 kHz, 10 kΩ. The resistors have been multiplied by 10^4 and the capacitors have been multiplied by

$$\frac{1}{2 \times \pi \times 2500 \times 10^4} = 6.366 \times 10^{-9}$$

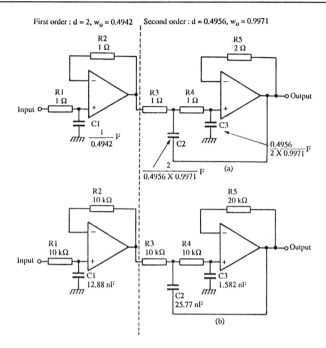

Figure 4.17 *Circuit diagram of the 3rd order Chebyshev low-pass active filter used as an example:*
a) has the normalized component values
b) has the 2.5 kHz, 10 k Ω component values

Figure 4.18 shows the amplitude response up to 3.5 kHz for this filter: 1 dB of passband ripple can be seen and the cut-off frequency is 2.5 kHz, as specified. Also shown are the individual responses of the first and second-order sections which make up the filter. These show how the highly peaked (small value of d) second-order section, which has a peak gain of more than 6 dB, is compensated for by the low-Q first-order section, whose 3 dB cut-off frequency is about 1.24 kHz. Since the attenuation values on the vertical axis are in dB, it is simply a matter of summing together the individual responses of the sections at any particular frequency to give the total response.

This illustrates why it is preferable to put the first-order section first in this example, and why in general the sections should be placed in order of descending d. As the d of a section becomes lower, the peak gain becomes greater and so, for a given level of input signal, the output of that section has to handle a larger signal, at least for part of the frequency range. There is

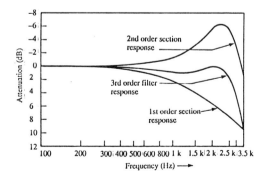

Figure 4.18 *Amplitude response of the 3rd order 1 dB pass-band ripple Chebyshev low-pass active filter shown in Fig. 4.17*
Also shown are the responses of the 1st and 2nd order sections which form the filter

Table 4.3 *0.01 dB passband ripple Chebyshev d and w_0 values*

FILTER	ORDER	d	w0
C02 04	02	1.3799	3.2289
C03 04	03	0.8781	1.8100
		2.0000	1.5894
C04 04	04	0.5801	1.4164
		1.7405	1.1398
C05 04	05	0.4028	1.2539
		1.3135	1.0066
		2.0000	0.8172
C06 04	06	0.2928	1.1713
		0.9669	0.9690
		1.7994	0.7113
C07 04	07	0.2212	1.1235
		0.7248	0.9608
		1.4229	0.7072
		2.0000	0.5584
C08 04	08	0.1725	1.0934
		0.5584	0.9617
		1.0915	0.7364
		1.8190	0.5212
C09 04	09	0.1380	1.0732
		0.4417	0.9653
		0.8469	0.7714
		1.4661	0.5466
		2.0000	0.4264
C10 04	10	0.1128	1.0589
		0.3576	0.9693
		0.6718	0.8036
		1.1468	0.5931
		1.8278	0.4125

Table 4.4 *0.025 dB passband ripple Chebyshev d and w_0 values*

FILTER	ORDER	d	w0
C02 07	02	1.3596	2.5690
C03 07	03	0.8361	1.5788
		2.0000	1.3201
C04 07	04	0.5378	1.2984
		1.7039	0.9893
C05 07	05	0.3671	1.1821
		1.2406	0.9156
		2.0000	0.7021
C06 07	06	0.2640	1.1230
		0.8901	0.9100
		1.7604	0.6285
C07 07	07	0.1981	1.0887
		0.6570	0.9198
		1.3425	0.6505
		2.0000	0.4846
C08 07	08	0.1537	1.0671
		0.5014	0.9317
		1.0036	0.6968
		1.7794	0.4635
C09 07	09	0.1226	1.0526
		0.3943	0.9424
		0.7668	0.7425
		1.3828	0.5050
		2.0000	0.3716
C10 07	10	0.1000	1.0423
		0.3179	0.9512
		0.6026	0.7816
		1.0541	0.5631
		1.7880	0.3680

Table 4.5 *0.05 dB passband ripple Chebyshev d and w_0 values*

FILTER	ORDER	d	w0
C02 10	02	1.3364	2.1618
C03 10	03	0.7956	1.4294
		2.0000	1.1371
C04 10	04	0.5004	1.2210
		1.6662	0.8853
C05 10	05	0.3371	1.1348
		1.1733	0.8536
		2.0000	0.6190
C06 10	06	0.2406	1.0909
		0.8242	0.8701
		1.7207	0.5693
C07 10	07	0.1797	1.0656
		0.6011	0.8924
		1.2687	0.6110
		2.0000	0.4302
C08 10	08	0.1390	1.0496
		0.4557	0.9117
		0.9284	0.6697
		1.7390	0.4217
C09 10	09	0.1106	1.0389
		0.3568	0.9270
		0.7010	0.7229
		1.3066	0.4758
		2.0000	0.3308
C10 10	10	0.0900	1.0313
		0.2869	0.9391
		0.5472	0.7668
		0.9749	0.5424
		1.7474	0.3354

Table 4.6 *0.1 dB passband ripple Chebyshev d and w_0 values*

FILTER	ORDER	d	w0
C02 15	02	1.3032	1.8204
C03 15	03	0.7458	1.2999
		2.0000	0.9694
C04 15	04	0.4581	1.1533
		1.6160	0.7893
C05 15	05	0.3047	1.0931
		1.0935	0.7974
		2.0000	0.5389
C06 15	06	0.2158	1.0627
		0.7510	0.8345
		1.6682	0.5132
C07 15	07	0.1604	1.0452
		0.5414	0.8679
		1.1815	0.5746
		2.0000	0.3768
C08 15	08	0.1237	1.0342
		0.4077	0.8938
		0.8453	0.6451
		1.6858	0.3816
C09 15	09	0.0982	1.0267
		0.3180	0.9134
		0.6309	0.7054
		1.2166	0.4487
		2.0000	0.2905
C10 15	10	0.0799	1.0215
		0.2550	0.9284
		0.4893	0.7536
		0.8875	0.5235
		1.6939	0.3041

Table 4.7 *0.25 dB passband ripple Chebyshev d and w_0 values*

FILTER	ORDER	d	w0
C02 24	02	1.2357	1.4540
C03 24	03	0.6631	1.1570
		2.0000	0.7672
C04 24	04	0.3943	1.0779
		1.5215	0.6744
C05 24	05	0.2580	1.0466
		0.9653	0.7324
		2.0000	0.4370
C06 24	06	0.1811	1.0311
		0.6428	0.7939
		1.5698	0.4441
C07 24	07	0.1339	1.0223
		0.4565	0.8402
		1.0421	0.5319
		2.0000	0.3076
C08 24	08	0.1029	1.0168
		0.3411	0.8737
		0.7229	0.6169
		1.5863	0.3316
C09 24	09	0.0815	1.0131
		0.2648	0.8981
		0.5316	0.6854
		1.0729	0.4166
		2.0000	0.2378
C10 24	10	0.0661	1.0105
		0.2117	0.9163
		0.4090	0.7387
		0.7588	0.5018
		1.5938	0.2648

Table 4.8 *0.5 dB passband ripple Chebyshev d and w_0 values*

FILTER	ORDER	d	w0
C02 32	02	1.1578	1.2313
C03 32	03	0.5861	1.0689
		2.0000	0.6265
C04 32	04	0.3401	1.0313
		1.4182	0.5970
C05 32	05	0.2200	1.0177
		0.8490	0.6905
		2.0000	0.3623
C06 32	06	0.1535	1.0114
		0.5524	0.7681
		1.4628	0.3962
C07 32	07	0.1131	1.0080
		0.3883	0.8227
		0.9161	0.5039
		2.0000	0.2562
C08 32	08	0.0867	1.0059
		0.2885	0.8610
		0.6209	0.5989
		1.4780	0.2967
C09 32	09	0.0686	1.0046
		0.2233	0.8885
		0.4519	0.6727
		0.9430	0.3954
		2.0000	0.1984
C10 32	10	0.0556	1.0037
		0.1782	0.9087
		0.3459	0.7293
		0.6516	0.4878
		1.4850	0.2372

Table 4.9   *1 dB passand ripple Chebyshev d and w_0 values*

FILTER	ORDER	d	w0
C02 45	02	1.0455	1.0500
C03 45	03	0.4956	0.9971
		2.0000	0.4942
C04 45	04	0.2810	0.9932
		1.2746	0.5286
C05 45	05	0.1800	0.9941
		0.7149	0.6552
		2.0000	0.2895
C06 45	06	0.1249	0.9954
		0.4550	0.7468
		1.3143	0.3531
C07 45	07	0.0918	0.9963
		0.3169	0.8084
		0.7710	0.4801
		2.0000	0.2054
C08 45	08	0.0702	0.9971
		0.2344	0.8506
		0.5111	0.5838
		1.3279	0.2651
C09 45	09	0.0555	0.9976
		0.1809	0.8806
		0.3686	0.6622
		0.7936	0.3773
		2.0000	0.1593
C10 45	10	0.0449	0.9980
		0.1442	0.9025
		0.2809	0.7215
		0.5363	0.4761
		1.3342	0.2121

therefore a risk of forcing the output towards the supply rails, clipping the output waveform. By putting the first-order section first, the input signal is attenuated before reaching the second-order section, especially at the frequency where this section has maximum gain, and so there is much less chance of the output clipping.

Bessel low-pass active filter design

As was seen in Fig. 4.13, the basic second-order section can be used to implement the Bessel approximation by setting the value of d to 1.732. Bessel filters of greater complexities can be built up section by section, exactly as for the Butterworth and Chebyshev approximations. Table 4.10 gives the values of d and ω_0 for the first and second-order sections which comprise the filters for orders from 2 to 9. These filters have their normalized cut-off frequencies defined as the 3 dB attenuation point, as in Chapter 2.

The attenuation curves of Fig. 2.24 can be used to estimate the order of an active Bessel filter required to satisfy a particular specification, exactly as in the passive case, remembering that the Bessel approximation is best when a linear phase response is needed. Let us say that a fourth-order Bessel low-pass filter is required, and the 3 dB cut-off frequency and impedance level must be set to 500 Hz and 10 k Ω respectively.

Table 4.10 gives the following values for the two second-order sections

Section 1	Section 2
$d = 1.9160$	$d = 1.2414$
$\omega_0 = 1.4192$	$\omega_0 = 1.5912$

The normalized value for C_1 is therefore given by

$$C_1 = \frac{2}{1.9160 \times 1.4192} = 0.7355 \, \text{F}$$

The values of the remaining capacitors can be found in the same way and expressions for their normalized values are shown in Fig. 4.19(a). Figure 4.19 (b) shows the components scaled to 500 Hz, 10 k Ω. The resistors have been multiplied by 10^4 and the capacitors have been multiplied by

$$\frac{1}{2 \times \pi \times 500 \times 10^4} = 3.1831 \times 10^{-8}$$

Figure 4.20 shows the amplitude response of the scaled filter. The 3 dB attenuation point is accurately placed at 500 Hz and the filter achieves an attenuation point of 14 dB at twice, 35 dB at four times, and 58 dB at eight times the cut-off frequency. This is the expected roll-off rate of a fourth-order Bessel filter, being worse than the same order Butterworth filter from the amplitude-response point of view.

Table 4.10 *Bessel d and w_0 values*

FILTER	ORDER	d	W_O
G02	02	1.7321	1.2736
G03	03	1.4471	1.4524
		2.0000	1.3270
G04	04	1.2414	1.5912
		1.9160	1.4192
G05	05	1.0911	1.7607
		1.7745	1.5611
		2.0000	1.5069
G06	06	0.9772	1.9071
		1.6361	1.6913
		1.9596	1.6060
G07	07	0.8879	2.0507
		1.5132	1.8235
		1.8784	1.7174
		2.0000	1.6853
G08	08	0.8158	2.1953
		1.4068	1.9591
		1.7870	1.8376
		1.9763	1.7838
G09	09	0.7564	2.3235
		1.3148	2.0815
		1.6966	1.9488
		1.9242	1.8794
		2.0000	1.8575

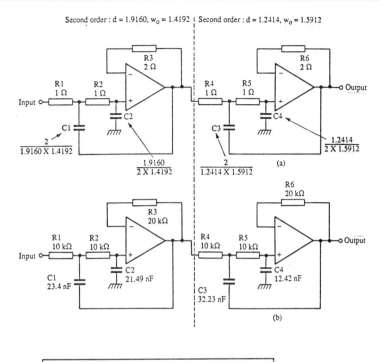

Figure 4.19 *Circuit diagrams for the 4th order Bessel low-pass active filter:*
a) has the normalized component values
b) has the 500 Hz, 10k Ω component values

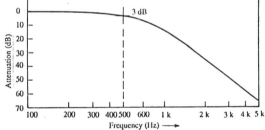

Figure 4.20 *Amplitude response of the 4th order Bessel low-pass active filter shown in Fig. 4.19 (b)*

Variable cut-off frequency low-pass filters

With the two types of Sallen and Key second-order sections shown, the cut-off frequency can be varied by altering the capacitor values for a given impedance level. The converse is also true: if the capacitor values are kept constant and the resistor values are varied, the cut-off frequency will vary. The impedance level will also vary, but most of the time with active filters this is unimportant. This feature of active filters gives them a major advantage over passive filters, where designing circuits with continuously variable cut-off frequencies, especially at audio frequencies, is very difficult.

Figure 4.21 shows the third-order, 1 dB passband-ripple, Chebyshev low-pass filter from Fig. 4.17 (b) with its $10\,k\Omega$ resistors replaced by ganged $22\,k\Omega$ variable resistors. The responses obtained from the circuit as these resistors are varied are shown in Fig. 4.22. Values of $20\,k\Omega$, $10\,k\Omega$ and $5\,k\Omega$

Figure 4.21 *The 3rd order Chebyshev low-pass filter from Fig. 4.17, with the cut-off frequency determining resistors replaced by ganged 22 kΩ variable resistors*

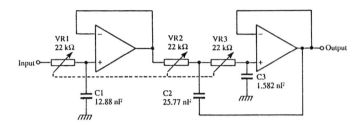

Figure 4.22 *Amplitude responses of the 3rd order 1 dB pass-band ripple Chebyshev low-pass filter for three values for the variable resistors*

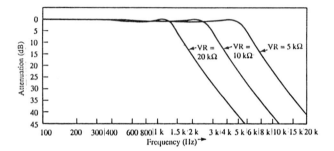

give cut-off frequencies of 1.25 kHz, 2.5 kHz and 5 kHz respectively. The overall shape of the response remains the same, an attenuation of about 23 dB being achieved at twice the cut-off frequency. In the pass band, the magnitude of the ripples is constant, and they are stretched or compressed on the frequency scale as the cut-off frequency is changed.

From the practical point of view, it would be best to include some fixed resistance, of say 1 kΩ, in series with each variable resistor so that the total resistance for each combination is never zero. Three-gang potentiometers (or more, if a variable cut-off frequency filter of even higher order is required) are not easy to obtain, and some suitable mechanical arrangement of pairing stereo controls may be needed. Alternatively, a multi-pole switch could be used to provide, say, three different cut-off frequencies suitable for CW, SSB and broadcast station reception in a general-coverage receiver. A 4-pole, 3-way switch would allow control of up to a fourth-order filter. Another possibility is an electronic means of varying the resistors, such as by using matched FETs with their resistance controlled by the gate voltage.

State-variable active filter sections

So far, the two implementations shown for second-order sections have used Sallen and Key single op-amp circuits. One obvious drawback with these circuits is that the gain is not independently variable: the circuit of Fig. 4.12 has a gain fixed at 1, and the circuit of Fig. 4.14 has its gain fixed at $3 - d$. In some cases, it may not be possible to adjust the gain elsewhere in the system, and so active filter sections where the gain, cut-off frequency and damping

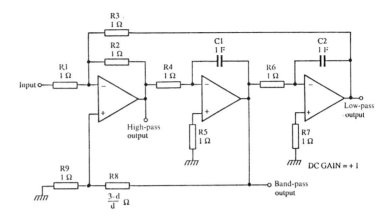

Figure 4.23 *The normalized, unity gain, second-order, state-variable active section. Note that this section has high-pass and band-pass outputs, as well as a low-pass output*

factor are all independently variable would be useful. Another, not so obvious, drawback of the Sallen and Key circuits is that small variations in the component values produce larger variations in the response than with some other implementations. This effect is known as sensitivity and is important where filters with highly accurate responses are required.

One circuit which overcomes some of these problems is the state-variable, or biquad, configuration. Figure 4.23 shows the unity-gain version of this configuration. At first sight, the fact that it uses three op-amps rather than the single one of Sallen and Key circuits may make it seem unattractive. However, 14-pin dual-in-line packages which contain 4 op-amps are now cheap, and so this circuit does not necessarily have to occupy a great deal more board space, or be any more expensive, than the single op-amp implementations.

The state-variable configuration uses the general-purpose summing circuit and the simple integrator building blocks which were described early in this chapter. The frequency-determining components are R_4 and R_6, and C_1 and C_2, which should be kept equal at all times. Resistances R_1, R_2 and R_3 should also be kept equal. The value of R_8 determines the damping factor obtained from the circuit. As well as being less sensitive to component variations than

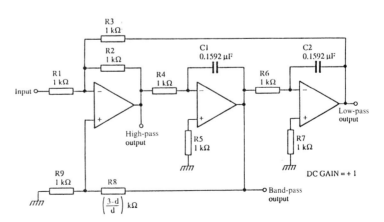

Figure 4.24 *The unity gain, second-order, state-variable active section scaled to 1 kHz, 1 kΩ*

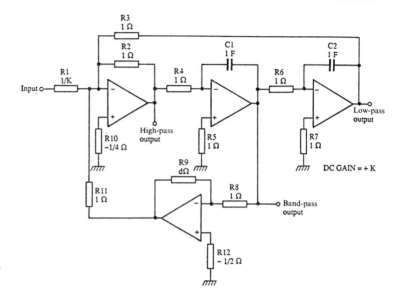

Figure 4.25 *The normalized, variable gain, second-order, state-variable active section*

the Sallen and Key circuits, this configuration produces a high-pass and a band-pass output, as well as the desired low-pass output. These outputs will be explained in the next chapter, where responses other than low-pass will be considered. Figure 4.24 shows this unity-gain section scaled to 1 kHz and 1 kΩ. It only remains to set R_8 for the value of d required.

The addition of another op-amp allows a variable-gain, state-variable section to be implemented, as shown in Fig.4.25: since we will usually be using packages containing four op-amps, this circuit is just as easy to build as the unity-gain section. With the four op-amps circuit we have finally achieved the aim of separate control of DC gain, cut-off frequency and damping factor: R_1 determines the DC gain, and its normalized value is $1/k\,\Omega$; the cut-off frequency is determined by R_4, R_6, C_1 and C_2 as before; and R_9 sets the damping factor. Resistors R_{10} and R_{12} are chosen to equalize DC offsets into the inverting and non-inverting inputs of the op-amps, which explains their rather strange values. They can be omitted if offsets are not a problem.

Switched-capacitor and switched-resistor filters

The cut-off frequency of an active low-pass filter can be made variable by substituting potentiometers for the response determining resistors, as shown in Fig. 4.21. To implement even this comparatively simple third-order filter, some ingenuity is needed to obtain or devise a three-gang potentiometer, and, of course, the problem becomes worse as higher-order filters are required. In this section, two solutions to this problem are presented, one which has been adopted by professional integrated circuit designers, and the other more suitable for use in non-integrated designs.

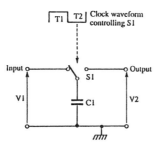

Figure 4.26 *A basic switched capacitor circuit*

Figure 4.6 showed the basic op-amp integrator and Fig. 4.23 showed the normalized state-variable circuit, which uses two identical integrator sections to determine the frequency response of the total filter. The cut-off frequency of the low-pass output from the state-variable section depends critically on the relationship between the frequency-response-determining resistors and capacitors (R_4, R_6, C_1 in Fig. 4.23 in the integrators. If an integrated-circuit implementation of the state-variable stage were attempted, a major problem faced by the designer would be that accurate values for the components could not be guaranteed. On an IC, it is considerably easier to accurately match the ratio of two different-value components of the same type. Therefore, the circuit in its present form is not suitable for use on an IC. This problem has led to the development of the switched-capacitor filter, whose principle of operation will now be explained.

Figure 4.26 shows a capacitor, C_1, whose top terminal can be switched between the input voltage, V_1, and the output voltage, V_2, by a changeover switch, S_1. During time T_1, C_1 charges to V_1, and during the second half of the clock cycle, T_2, the switch changes over, causing C_1 to discharge to voltage V_2. The total charge, Q, transferred from input to output in one clock cycle $(T_1 + T_2)$ is given by

$$Q = C_1 (V_1 - V_2) \tag{4.11}$$

This process continues with a repetition time of $T_1 + \times T_2$, causing an average current, I, from input to output of

$$I = \frac{Q}{(T_1 + T_2)} = \frac{C_1 (V_1 - V_2)}{(T_1 + T_2)} \tag{4.12}$$

By using Ohms' law, where

$$R = V/I:$$

$$R = \frac{V}{I} = \frac{(V_1 + V_2)}{I} = \frac{(T_1 + T_2)}{C_1} \tag{4.13}$$

The interval $T_1 + T_2$ represents the period of the clock controlling the changeover switch, and so equation 4.13 can be re-written as

$$R = \frac{1}{C_1 \times f_{clk}} \tag{4.14}$$

where f_{clk} is the frequency of the clock.

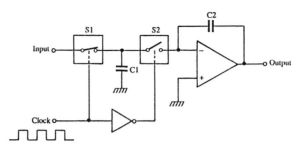

Figure 4.27 *A switched capacitor integrator circuit*

Equation 4.14 tells us that C_1 behaves as a resistor between the input and output terminals, and has a value inversely proportional to the clock frequency. Figure 4.27 shows the switched capacitor incorporated into the op-amp integrator circuit. The response of the integrator now depends on the ratio of two capacitor values, C_1 and C_2, one of which is behaving as a resistor, rather than on the absolute values of a resistor and a capacitor as before. It is relatively easy to fabricate two capacitors which have an accurately matched ratio and so we now have an integrator which is suitable for use in integrated circuits. It is only necessary to vary the frequency of the clock controlling the switches to vary the response of the integrator, and therefore the cut-off frequency of any filter into which it is incorporated. The frequency of the switching clock must be chosen to be well above the cut-off frequency of the filter, so as not to produce undesirable effects within the passband of the filter.

Several IC manufacturers market devices which use this technique. One notable range of switched-capacitor filters in the MF series of devices from National Semiconductor [8,9]. The MF5 and MF10 are so-called universal-filter building blocks, enabling filters of several different types and approximations to be devised. The MF4 and MF6 are more specialized devices, implementing fourth and sixth-order low-pass Butterworth responses. The MF5 and MF10 devices make use of the non-inverting integrator circuit shown in Fig. 4.28, where double-gang switches reverse the polarity of the switched capacitor between the charging and discharging cyles.

Although the switched-capacitor filter is very useful for use on integrated circuits, its use in filters constructed from discrete components is fairly limited. What is needed is a method of accurately controlling several resistance values, preferably by electronic means. One method is to place an electronic switch in series with a resistor, and to vary the proportion of time the switch is opened, thereby varying the effective value of the resistor.

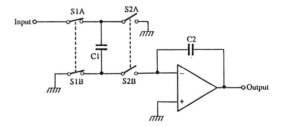

Figure 4.28 *The non-inverting integrator used in the National Semiconductors MF-series devices*

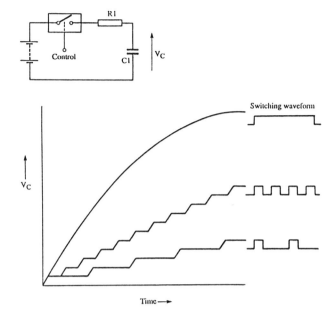

Figure 4.29 *Controlling the charging rate of a capacitor using an electronic switch*

Figure 4.30 *The charging waveform across C_1 for three switch control waveforms.*

Figure 4.29 shows this arrangement, where the charging of capacitor C_1 is controlled by a switch in series with a resistor, R_1. The voltage waveform seen across the capacitor for these different values of the on time of the switch is shown in Fig. 4.30. If the switch is left permanently closed, the capacitor charges at the normal time-constant rate; if the closed state of the switch is only permitted for a proportion of the time constant, the charging of the capacitor is restricted to the periods when the switch is closed, and so the time constant is effectively lengthened, as if the resistor had a higher value. The discrete steps in the charging waveform can be smoothed out by increasing the frequency of the switch control clock.

This technique as applied to the third-order Chebyshev low-pass filter originally shown in Fig. 4.17 (b), is shown in Fig. 4.31. CMOS analogue switches such as CD4016 or CD4066 devices are used as the switching elements, and the cut-off frequency of the filter is controlled by altering the mark/space ratio of the switching waveform. As in the switched capacitor case, the frequency of the switching clock should be well above the cut-off frequency of the filter, and a simple low-pass filter at the output of the controlled filter will

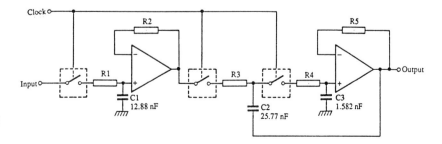

Figure 4.31 *The 3rd order Chebyshev low-pass filter adapted for switched resistor control*

eliminate the clock waveform from the output spectrum. Practical applications of this technique can be found in references 10 and 11.

The complex frequency plane representation

In this chapter, the responses of first and second-order sections have been described by the values of d and ω_0. The advantage of using these parameters is that the effect of varying them on a response can fairly easily be pictured, even by relatively inexperienced designers. One disadvantage, however, is that there is a large amount of data in filter literature which is in a different format, as the positions in the complex plane of the roots of the transfer functions which describe filter responses. The aim of this section, therefore, is to show how this complex plane information can be converted into the d and ω_0 format, so that it can be used to design filters as described in this chapter.

Figure 4.32 (a) shows how a third-order filter response can be plotted as three points in the complex plane. The horizontal axis represents the real part, and the vertical axis represents the imaginary part of the co-ordinates of the points. In the examples shown, the three points have the co-ordinates $-1+j0$, $-0.5+j0.866$ and $-0.5-j0.866$. One root is purely real, having no imaginary part, and the two complex roots are conjugates of each other,

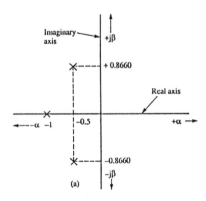

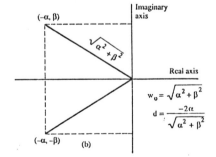

Figure 4.32 *A method of describing a filter response by the position of the roots of the filter's transfer function:*
a) Shows the position of the roots of a third-order filter
b) Shows how the position of the roots can be converted to the d and ω_0 format

meaning that their real parts are equal and their imaginary parts are of equal magnitude, but of opposite sign. The complex roots can be written as $-0.5 \pm j0.866$, and these complex roots always occur in pairs. A first-order filter has only one root, which will be purely real; a second-order filter has two complex conjugate roots; a third-order filter has one real and two complex conjugate roots; and so on.

Figure 4.32 (b) shows a generalized pair of complex conjugate roots, with co-ordinates $(-\alpha, -\beta)$ and $(-\alpha, +\beta)$. It is these values of α and β which are given in many catalogues of filter designs. The value of ω_0 for this pair of roots is simply the distance from the origin for the roots, and is given by:

$$\omega = \sqrt{\alpha^2 + \beta^2} \tag{4.15}$$

The damping factor d is given by

$$d = \frac{-2\alpha}{\sqrt{\alpha^2 + \beta^2}} \tag{4.16}$$

For the real root shown in Fig. 4.32 (a)

$$\omega_0 = \sqrt{(-1)^2 + (0)^2} = 1$$

and

$$d = \frac{-2(-1)}{1} = 2$$

For the complex pair of roots

$$\omega_0 = \sqrt{(-0.5)^2 + (\pm 0.866)^2} = 1$$

and

$$d = \frac{-2(-0.5)}{1} = 1$$

If these values for d and ω_0 are compared with those in Table 4.2, they can be seen to correspond to the third-order Butterworth filter. In general, of course, the values of d and ω_0 do not work out to be such nice whole numbers. The equations shown above can be used for all filter types, including the Butterworth, Chebyshev and Bessel approximations considered in this chapter. In Chapter 7, a BASIC program is given which performs this conversion.

Summary and conclusions

Active filters should not be seen as a completely new subject, but as an extension of the principles already learned for passive filters. Many of the concepts explained in previous chapters, such as normalization, scaling and filter approximations are still valid and useful. The commonest active elements used in active filters are op-amps and a brief introduction to the most commmonly used circuit configurations was given. No detailed derivations for the equations which govern the gain of the circuits were shown, but the equations themselves were presented, so that the circuits can be adapted for use in different situations.

Three first-order filter circuits were shown, all of which have the classical first-order roll-off rate of 6 dB/octave or 20 dB/decade: a unity-gain configuration which is produced by adding a capacitor to the non-inverting input of the op-amp in the voltage-follower circuit; a configuration with a DC gain of greater than 1, obtained by adding another resistor to the unity-gain circuit; and a modified op-amp integrator, which allows DC gains of less than 1 to be obtained.

The addition of another capacitor and resistor to a first-order circuit results in a second-order response being obtained. Two second-order circuits were described, both Sallen and Key configurations:

1. a unity-gain circuit, where the frequency determining resistors are equal in value;
2. an equal-capacitor value circuit, where the gain is related to the damping factor.

As was found with LC second-order networks, the responses of these circuits could be controlled by setting the damping factor d, and shifting the response up and down the frequency axis. By varying the damping factor, second-order Butterworth, Chebyshev and Bessel responses could be obtained.

The design method for Butterworth, Chebyshev and Bessel low-pass filters for orders from 2 to 10 was described. This involves the use of catalogues of values of d and ω_0, building filters out of cascaded first and second-order sections.

Since the cut-off frequency of active filters can be varied by changing resistor values only, low-pass filters with variable cut-off frequencies, but with the passband ripple and roll-off rate constant, can be designed. This is a major advantage that active filters have over passive filters: by using ganged potentiometers, a continously variable cut-off frequency can be obtained. Alternatively, multi-pole switches can allow discrete steps in the cut-off frequency by selecting different resistor values.

Important recent developments in the field of active filters are the switched-capacitor and switched-resistor methods of controlling the cut-off frequency of a filter. These techniques obviate the need for multi-ganged potentiometers and allow filters to be automatically locked to a varying frequency to provide, for example, elimination of a varying frequency in a communication channel.

Although the Sallen and Key circuits are useful, general-purpose implementations, independent control of the cut-off frequency, the gain and the damping factor of these filters can be obtained by use of state-variable configurations. Despite the fact that these configurations use three or four op-amps, compared with only one for the Sallen and Key circuits, this does not necessarily imply a great increase in the number of components or the cost of a filter. The state-variable configurations are also less sensitive to small variations in their components values than their Sallen and Key equivalents.

Finally, a brief introduction into the complex-plane representation of a filter response was given. A method of converting this representation into the d and ω_0 format was shown. This enables a great deal of published data which is in the complex-plane format to be used with the circuits shown in this chapter.

References

1. D. Lancaster, *Active Filter Cookbook*, 1980, Sams.
2. A.B. Williams, *Electronic Filter Design Handbook*, 1981, McGraw-Hill.
3. G.B. Clayton, *Operational Amplifiers*, 1979, Butterworths.
4. J.J. Carr, Linear *IC Op Amp Handbook*, 1983, Tab Books.
5. I.E. Shepherd, *Operational Amplifiers*, 1981, Longman.
6. J.B. Dance, *Op-amps: Their Principles and Application*, 1986, Newnes.
7. as reference 2: tables 12–22 to 12–26.
8. T. Regan, *Introducing the MF10: A Versatile Monolithic Active Filter Building Block (application note AN307)*, 1986, Linear Applications Data Book, published by National Semiconductor, pages 908–18.
9. *MF4, MF5, MF6 and MF10 Data Sheets, Linear Supplement Data Book*, 1984, National Semiconductor, pages S9.1–S9.27.
10. S. Price, *The G4BWE Tunable CW Filter*, September 1984, RadComm, pages 755–58.
11. S. Price, *The GW4BWE Versafilter*, July 1987, RadComm, pages 483–87.

5 Active high-pass, band-pass and band-stop filters

We can now design an equally extensive range of active and passive low-pass filters, although the upper frequency limit for the active filters is more limited. It is natural, then, to extend the design techniques for active low-pass filters to cover other responses, such as high-pass, band-pass and band-stop. Transformation is again a useful technique in obtaining these responses, particularly the high-pass response, but can be difficult to apply to band-pass and band-stop filters. There are sections available which are designed specifically to give a band-pass response, and these can also be used in the design of band-stop filters. State-variable sections, which were first discussed in Chapter 4, have several outputs, each producing a specific response; these allow the implementation of different responses by simply selecting the correct output. In the case of band-pass filters, cascading of low-pass and high-pass sections is a viable design method, and the chances of success are higher than for passive filters because of the inherent isolation of active sections resulting from the use of op-amps. Similarly, band-stop filters can be produced from combinations of low-pass and high-pass filters connected in parallel, although in practice there are few applications for this type of filter.

It is generally easier to vary the cut-off frequency of active low-pass filters than that of the passive low-pass type and this is also true for other responses. This property of active filters enables circuits with switchable or continuously variable cut-off frequencies to be produced and can lead to some very versatile and useful designs. Several examples of these designs will be described in this chapter.

The active low-pass to high-pass transformation

Active high-pass filters can be derived directly from normalized low-pass configurations by means of a transformation, in a similar manner to passive filters. Once more, the transformation is simple: in the normalized low-pass design, the response-determining resistors are transformed into capacitors, and capacitors are transformed into resistors. Each transformed component has the value of the reciprocal of the normalized low-pass prototype component. The transformation is shown in Fig. 5.1, where the low-pass prototype components have the subscript L, and the transformed high-pass components have the subscript H. It is important to realise that only resistors that are part of the response-determining RC networks are transformed, all other

102

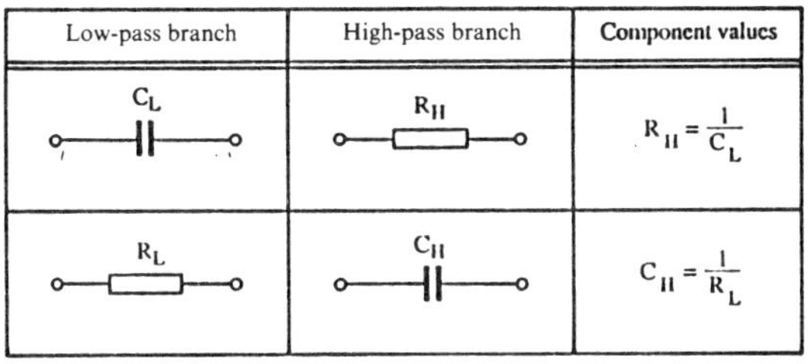

Low-pass branch	High-pass branch	Component values
C_L	R_H	$R_H = \dfrac{1}{C_L}$
R_L	C_H	$C_H = \dfrac{1}{R_L}$

Figure 5.1 *Active low-pass to high-pass branch transformations. Only the response determining components are transformed; the op-amps themselves and any gain setting resistors remain unaltered*

resistors which determine, for example, the gain of the section are unaltered. Only after the high-pass components have been calculated in their normalized form are they scaled to suit the final cut-off frequency and impedance level.

The results of applying the transformation to two typical first-order filter sections are shown in Fig. 5.2. Transformation of the unity-gain, first-order low-pass configuration results in a unity-gain, first-order high-pass section. Similarly, the first-order low-pass section based on the non-inverting amplifier with gain results in a high-pass first-order section with gain.

Second-order Sallen and Key low-pass section transformations are shown in Figs. 5.3 and 5.4. As would be expected, the unity-gain low-pass configuration results in a unity-gain high-pass configuration. Because this configuration has equal resistor values in the low-pass prototype, an equal capacitor value high-pass filter results when the transformation is applied. The transformed capacitors result in non-equal high-pass resistor values. The equal component value low-pass circuit of Fig. 5.4 gives an equal component value high-pass circuit when transformed, which has a gain at infinite frequency identical to the gain at DC for the low-pass prototype, given by $3 - d$.

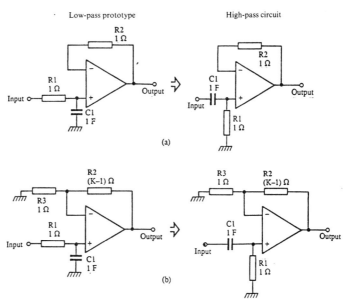

Figure 5.2 *Active low-pass to high-pass transformation of the first order sections:*
a) are the unity gain sections
b) are the sections with gain

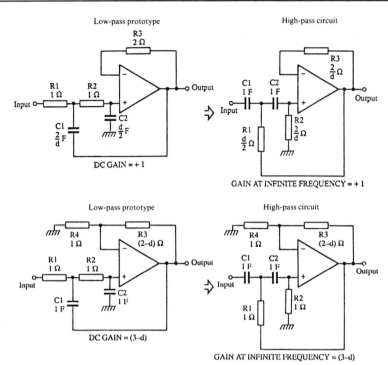

Figure 5.3 *Active low-pass to high-pass transformation of the unity gain Sallen and Key second order section, showing the normalized component values*

Figure 5.4 *Active low-pass to high-pass transformation of the equal component values Sallen and Key second order section, showing the normalized component values*

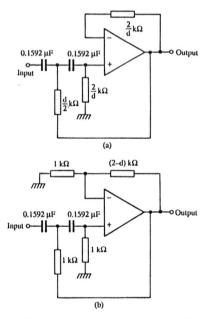

Figure 5.5 *The Sallen and Key second order active sections scaled to 1 kHz, 1 k Ω*
a) is the unity gain section
b) is the equal component values section

Figure 5.5 shows these two Sallen and Key high-pass circuits scaled to 1 kHz, 1 kΩ. In the unity-gain section, *d* can be seen in the expressions for all the resistors, whereas the equal-component section only has *d* in the expression for the feedback resistors. The effect of various values of *d* on the response is identical to the low-pass case, except of course that the high-pass response is the mirror image of the low-pass response. Fig. 5.6 shows these circuits with component values calculated for $d = 1.045$ which should, from Fig. 4.13 and equation 4.9, result in a Chebyshev response with a peak ripple of 1 dB; the amplitude responses of these circuits are shown in Fig. 5.7. The responses are similar, except that the equal component value circuit has a gain tending towards a value of $3 - d = 3 - 1.045 = 1.955$, or 5.8 dB at infinite frequency. The frequency at which the response first passes through this attenuation value is the reciprocal of that for the low-pass equivalent.

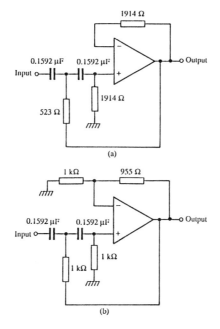

Figure 5.6 *The Sallen and Key second order active sections scaled to 1 kHz, 1 k Ω:*
a) is the unity gain section
b) is the equal component values section

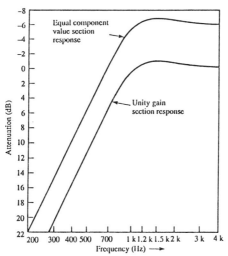

Figure 5.7 *Amplitude response of the 2nd order Sallen and Key high-pass active sections, scaled to 1 kHz, 1 k Ω*

The sections of Fig. 5.6 can therefore be used to implement the high-pass response for the Butterworth, Chebyshev and Bessel approximations by setting the appropriate value of d. Active high-pass filter design for orders greater than 2 proceeds in the same way as for low-pass filters, building up the required complexity from cascaded first and second-order sections.

Active high-pass filter design follows exactly the same procedure as for a passive high-pass filter, as described in Chapter 3. Briefly, this procedure relies on the conversion of the high-pass requirement into an equivalent low-pass requirement; the selection of a low-pass prototype filter which satisfies this requirement; the transformation of this low-pass prototype into a high-pass filter; and finally, scaling of this high-pass filter to meet the original frequency specification. This procedure will be illustrated with an example.

An active high-pass filter is required with a cut-off frequency of 100 Hz, and it must have an attenuation of at least 30 dB at 50 Hz, continuing to increase as frequency decreases. A ripple of 1 dB is allowed in the passband. Normalizing the 100 Hz cut-off frequency to 1 rad/s, the frequency at which the stopband attenuation is specified, ω_s, is 0.5 rad/s, equivalent to 2 rad/s for the low-pass prototype. Since 1 dB of ripple is allowed and a monotonic response is required, a Chebyshev filter will be selected. Reference to Fig. 2.14, the nomograph for Chebyshev filters, gives a theoretical order of about 3.5, so a fourth-order filter must be used. Figure 5.8 (a) shows this fourth-order low-pass filter, built up from two second-order sections, with the normalized component values incorporating values of d and ω_0 taken from Table 4.9. Fig. 5.8. (b) shows this low-pass prototype transformed into

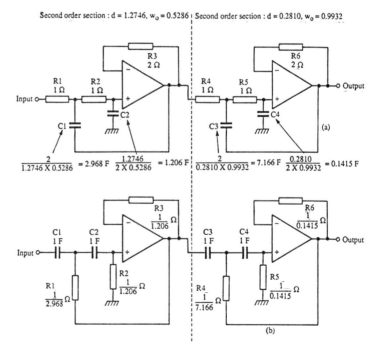

Figure 5.8 *Stages in the design of the 4th order 1 dB pass band ripple Chebyshev active high-pass filter:*
a) is the normalized low-pass prototype
b) is the transformed high-pass filter

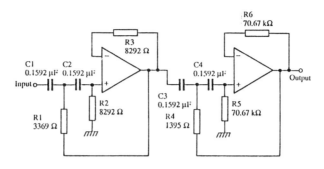

Figure 5.9 *The 4th order Chebyshev high-pass filter scaled to 100 Hz, 10 k Ω*

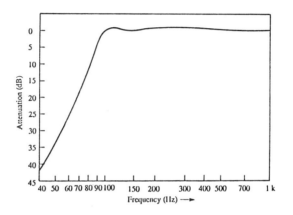

Figure 5.10 *Amplitude response of the 4th order 1 dB pass-band ripple Chebyshev high-pass active filter*

the normalized high-pass filter. Fig. 5.9. is the final circuit with components scaled to 100 Hz, 10 kΩ. Resistors have been multiplied by 10^4 and capacitors have been multiplied by

$$\frac{1}{2 \times \pi \times 100 \times 10^4} = 1.592 \times 10^{-7}$$

Note that d and ω_0 are incorporated into the expressions for the capacitors at the normalized low-pass stage, exactly as they would be if no transformation were about to be applied. Only when the normalized low-pass requirement has been met are the components transformed.

Figure 5.10 shows the amplitude response of the scaled high-pass filter. The ripple cut-off frequency of 100 Hz, and the passband ripple value of 1 dB have been met exactly. The pattern of ripples characteristic of a fourth-order Chebyshev filter, consisting of four half cycles, can be seen. At 50 Hz, an attenuation of approximately 33 dB is achieved, better than the 30 dB requirement because of the rounding of the filter order, and the attenuation continues to increase at lower frequencies, as specified.

Switchable cut-off frequencies

Active high-pass filters with switchable cut-off frequencies are easy to design using the transformed Sallen and Key equal component value section. The

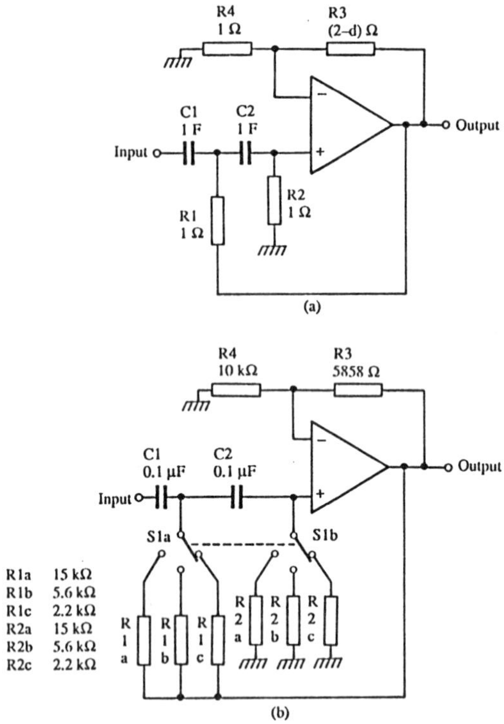

Figure 5.11 *Design of a second order Butterworth active high-pass filter with switchable cut-off frequences of 100, 300 and 700 Hz*
a) is the normalized Sallen and Key section
b) is the final design

normalized version of this section is shown in Fig. 5.11 (a). We will attempt to adapt this circuit into a second-order Butterworth filter, with its cut-off frequency selectable between 100, 300, and 700 Hz. With this design, we will set the capacitor values to 0.1 μ F and then calculate the correct impedance level. Equation 5.1 shows the expression for C_1 and C_2, somewhat simplified from its general form because ω_0 is 1 for a second-order Butterworth section

$$C_1 = C_2 = \frac{1}{2\pi f_C R} \tag{5.1}$$

where f_c is the cut-off frequency,
    R is the impedance level.

Re-arranging this equation to give R,

$$R = \frac{1}{2\pi f_c C_1} \tag{5.2}$$

Substituting $C_1 = 0.1 \, \mu$F, and calculating R for cut-off frequencies of 100, 300 and 700 Hz gives the component values shown in Table 5.1. If R_1 and R_2 are rounded to the nearest preferred value, while still keeping them equal, we would expect only a slight shift in the cut-off frequency, and the Butterworth approximation to remain valid. These rounded values for R_1 and R_2 are also shown in Table 5.1, along with the re-calculated cut-off frequencies: the cir-

Table 5.1 *Values of R_1 and R_2 for different cut-off frequencies for the second order Butterworth high-pass filter. The effect of rounding the values of R_1 and R_2 on the cut-off frequency can be seen*

NOMINAL CUT-OFF FREQUENCY (Hz)	EXACT VALUE OF R1,R2 (ohm)	ROUNDED VALUE OF R1,R2 (ohm)	ACTUAL CUT-OFF FREQUENCY (Hz)
100	15915	15k	106
300	5305	5.6k	284
700	2274	2.2k	723

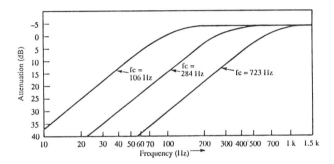

Figure 5.12 *Amplitude response of the 2nd order Butterworth high-pass filter with switchable cut-off frequencies. The rounded values for R_1 and R_2 have been used*

cuit diagram of the final filter is shown in Fig. 5.11 (b). Switching between the three cut-off frequencies is performed by S_1, a 2-pole 3-way switch. Resistor R_3 has been determined by calculating $2-d$, which for the second-order Butterworth response is $2-1.4142=0.5858$. The exact values of R_3 and R_4 are not critical so long as their ratio is maintained, and so both have been scaled to $10\,k\Omega$ impedance level.

The simulated amplitude responses of the filter for the three positions of S_1 are shown in Fig. 5.12. The low-pass form of this Sallen and Key section has a DC gain of $3-d$, which translates into the same gain at infinite frequency for the high-pass version. This can be seen from Fig. 5.12 as a shift up the attenuation scale of $3-1.4142=1.5858$ or $4\,dB$. The cut-off frequencies achieved for the switch positions correspond to the values calculated for the rounded resistor values, indicating that the technique is valid. In practice, the difference between the cut-off frequencies which would have been achieved with exact resistor values, and those achieved with rounded values would be undetectable. The considerable simplification made possible by rounding these resistors makes the design much more attractive to implement.

The state-variable high-pass sections

The state-variable section, first met in Chapter 4, has a high-pass, as well as a low-pass, output. Fig. 5.13 shows a state-variable section scaled to $1\,kHz$, $1\,k\Omega$. The values of R_8 corresponding to d values of 0.886 and 1.414 are

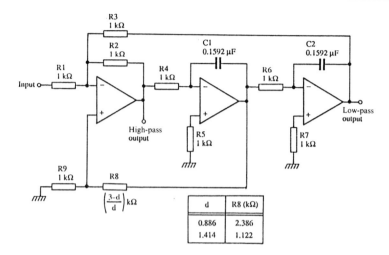

Figure 5.13 *The unity gain, second order state variable section scaled to 1 kHz, 1 k Ω showing the high-pass and low-pass outputs*

d	R8 (kΩ)
0.886	2.386
1.414	1.122

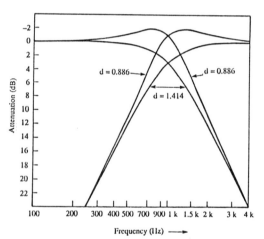

Figure 5.14 *High-pass and low-pass outputs of the unity gain state variable section for values of d of 0.886 and 1.414*

shown in Fig. 5.13 and the amplitude responses of the circuit for these two values are shown in Fig. 5.14. Both the low-pass and high-pass outputs are shown, and the symmetry between these responses can clearly be seen. When $d = 0.886$, high-pass and low-pass Chebyshev responses with peak amplitudes of 2 dB are obtained, and when $d = 1.414$ Butterworth responses are obtained. One advantage that the state-variable section, and the section with a fourth op-amp added to allow control over the gain, have over other high-pass sections is that they allow straightforward switching between a low-pass and a high-pass response, by simply selecting the correct output.

Active band-pass filters

When passive band-pass filters were discussed in Chapter 3, it was found that they could broadly be divided into three categories, depending on the centre frequency of the filter response relative to the passband bandwidth, the so-called band-pass Q. Large values of band-pass Q, that is where the passband is relatively narrow, could be implemented using the tuned-circuit approach; medium values of band-pass Q could be accommodated using the low-pass to band-pass transformation; and low-band-pass Q filters could be designed using cascaded low-pass and high-pass filters, which also had the advantage of allowing asymmetrical band-pass responses to be implemented. With active filters, two approaches will be considered: the first is similar to the passive tuned circuit technique, there being active sections available with relatively narrow peaks to the amplitude response and controllable band-pass Q. The second is the cascading approach, which because of the inherent isolation of active sections from each other, is rather more versatile for active than for passive filters, allowing much narrower bandwidths to be achieved without fear of interaction.

The multiple-feedback band-pass filter

The circuit of Fig. 5.15 (a) is the multiple-feedback band-pass (MFBP) filter configuration, normalized to 1 rad/s and 1 Ω. The circuit effectively simulates the behaviour of a tuned circuit, having a peak in its amplitude response and increasing attenuation on either side of this peak. Because the peak in the amplitude response is identical to that obtained from a tuned circuit, it is convenient to refer to the frequency at which it occurs as the resonant frequency of the section. The expressions for R_1 and R_2 contain the quantity Q,

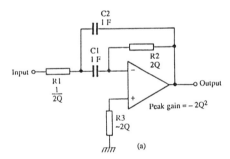

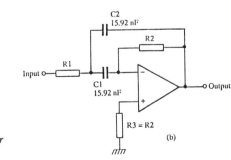

Figure 5.15 *The multiple feedback band-pass filter configuration*
a) is the normalized circuit
b) is scaled to 1 kHz, 10 kΩ.
Table 5.2 shows resistor values for various values of Q.

which is the band-pass Q we are already familiar with, having met it in Chapter 3, but it is worth repeating the expression for band-pass Q

$$Q_{bp} = \frac{f_r}{BW_{3dB}} \tag{5.3}$$

where f_r is the centre frequency of the response,
BW_{3dB} is the 3 dB attenuation bandwidth.

At the frequency where the peak occurs, the gain of the circuit is $2Q^2$, and the input signal is inverted.

Figure 5.15 (b) shows the circuit scaled to 1 kHz, 10 kΩ. The values of R_1 and R_2 cannot be calculated until the band-pass Q is decided upon and Table 5.2 shows the values of R_1 and R_2 for four values of band-pass Q. The resistor R_3 is incorporated into the circuit to reduce op-amp output offset effects, and should be set equal to R_2 for best results. If high input-impedance op-amps, such as BIFETs are used, this will not be a problem. The resistor can be omitted and the non-inverting input of the op-amp connected directly to ground.

Also shown in Table 5.2 is the peak gain for different band-pass Q values and it can be seen that this gain soon gets out of hand, even for fairly moderate values of band-pass Q. For example, a band-pass Q of 10 gives a peak gain of 200 (or 46 dB), which means that an input voltage of 100 mV peak-to-peak at the resonant frequency would result in an output of 20 volts peak-to-peak if the op-amp supply rails would allow such a swing. Another potential problem is that higher values of band-pass Q result in lower values for R_1 and higher values for R_2. The first effect lowers the input impedance of the stage, perhaps leading to loading problems of the preceding stage, and the second results in the possibility of greater offsets at the op-amp output.

The amplitude responses obtained for this scaled circuit are shown in Fig. 5.16, plotted for band-pass Q values of 2, 5, 10 and 20. The increase in peak gain for increasing band-pass Q can clearly be seen. With a band-pass Q of 20, the peak gain is 58 dB at resonance. An increase in band-pass Q also

Table 5.2 *Resistor values and corresponding circuit peak gains for various band-pass Q values for the multiple feedback filter*

BANDPASS Q	NORMALISED		SCALED TO 10kohm		CIRCUIT GAIN	
	R1(ohm)	R2(ohm)	R1(kohm)	R2(kohm)	TIMES	dB
2	0.25	4	2.5	40	8	18.06
5	0.1	10	1.0	100	50	33.98
10	0.05	20	0.5	200	200	46.02
20	0.025	40	0.25	400	800	58.06

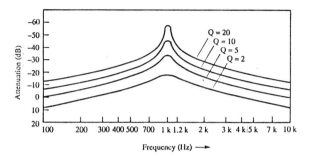

Figure 5.16 *Amplitude response of the MFBP section for band-pass Q values of 2, 5, 10 and 20. Note the increase in the peak gain for increasing Q. This is a major drawback of this configuration*

gives a greater initial roll-off rate close to the resonant frequency, but the ultimate roll-off well away from resonance is 6 dB/octave, implying a first-order response similar to that obtained in Chapter 3 for the parallel tuned circuit.

The dual-amplifier band-pass configuration

A rather better band-pass configuration than the single op-amp circuit is the dual amplifier band-pass (DABP) circuit, developed by Sedra and Espinoza, and shown in Fig. 5.17. Despite the use of an extra op-amp, the design procedure for this section is very simple. First of all, a value for C_1 and C_2 (which are identical) is chosen, and then the quantity R is calculated by

$$R = \frac{1}{2\pi f_r \times C} \tag{5.4}$$

where f_r is the resonant frequency,
  C is the value of C_1 and C_2.

The values of R_1, R_2 and R_3 are given by

$$R_1 = Q_{bp} \times R \tag{5.5}$$
$$R_2 = R_3 = R \tag{5.6}$$

where Q_{bp} is the band-pass Q required from the section.

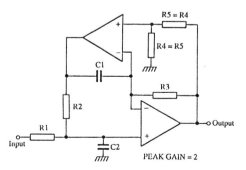

Figure 5.17 *The dual amplifier band-pass configuration*

Resistors R_4 and R_5 are made equal to each other and can be any reasonable value. The peak gain of the section at resonance is fixed at only 2, a considerable reduction on the MFBP or Sallen and Key circuits. Since dual op-amps are available in 8-pin dual-in-line packages, the DABP circuit does not have to be any more expensive or occupy more board space than the single op-amp circuits.

Let us say an active band-pass filter if required to peak the audio output of the detector in a CW receiver at 700 Hz. A band-pass Q of 10 and a peak gain of 2 are required. Because a peak gain of only 2 is required, the DABP section will be used. Choosing the value of C to be 0.22 μF and applying equations 5.4–5.6

$$R = \frac{1}{2 \times \pi \times 700 \times 0.22 \times 10^{-6}} = 1033 \, \Omega$$

$$R_1 = 10 \times R = 10.33 \, k\Omega$$
$$R_2 = R_3 = R = 1033 \, \Omega$$

If we choose R_4 and R_5 to be 4.7 kΩ, the values shown in Fig. 5.18 are obtained. Figure 5.19 shows the amplitude response of the filter. A band-pass Q of 10 coupled with a centre frequency of 700 Hz implies a 3 dB bandwidth of 70 Hz, and the response shows lower and upper cut-off frequencies of about 665 and 735 Hz, which gives the expected bandwidth. An attenuation of 30 dB with respect to the resonant frequency amplitude is achieved at 200 Hz and 2.5 kHz.

With the MFBP section, the ratio of the resistors R_1 and R_2 was $4Q^2$, which led to low values for R_1, the input resistor, and high values for R_2, the feedback resistor. With the DABP circuit, however, the ratio of the largest to the smallest resistor is only Q, a considerable improvement. Another benefit of this circuit is that the peak gain is only 2, compared with $2Q^2$ for the MFBP section, considerably reducing the possibility of clipping at the output. This circuit should be considered suitable for applications requiring band-pass Q values up to about 150, well worth the addition of an op-amp.

Two features of the DABP section make it attractive for applications demanding variable band-pass Q: firstly, the band-pass Q can be altered by varying only one resistor, R_1 and secondly, the peak amplitude remains constant at 2 (or 6 dB), no matter what the band-pass Q is set to. These features are exploited in the 700 Hz resonant frequency variable band-pass Q

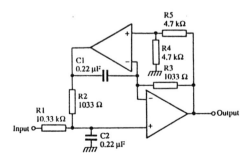

Figure 5.18 *The DABP circuit adapted into a Q = 10, 700 Hz centre frequency band-pass filter*

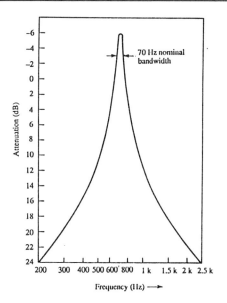

Figure 5.19 *Amplitude response of the Q = 10, f_c = 700 Hz DABP filter*

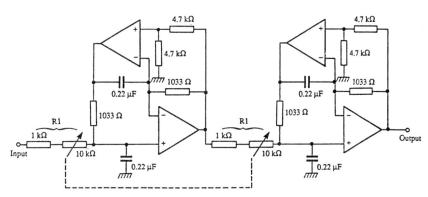

Figure 5.20 *Cascaded DABP sections with adjustable band-pass Q*

filter shown in Fig. 5.20. Here, two identical sections have been cascaded to increase the roll-off rate. Resistor R_1 for each section is composed of a fixed 1 kΩ resistor and a 10 kΩ potentiometer. At the lowest setting of the potentiometers, the band-pass Q of each section is about 1, and when the potentiometers are set to 10 kΩ, the band-pass Q is about 11. The filter can therefore be set to a low Q initially while a CW signal is located and tuned to give a 700 Hz beat frequency, and the band-pass Q then progressively increased to eliminate adjacent interfering signals.

The state-variable band-pass circuit

If even higher values of band-pass Q are required, or there is a need for simple control over the resonant frequency, a state-variable section should be used. This versatile section has already been met in the context of low-pass and

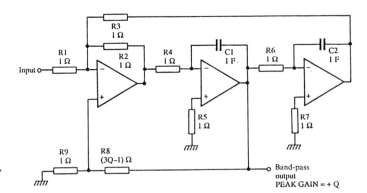

Figure 5.21 *The normalized state variable band-pass section*

high-pass filters and Fig. 5.21 shows the circuit in its normalized form. The expression for R_8 has been converted from its usual $(3-d)/d$ by substituting $d=1/Q$, to give $3Q-1$, a more useful format for band-pass filters. The peak gain of this section at resonance is Q, and cannot be altered within the section.

What exactly does this section offer over the other sections already described? First of all, the two resistors which determine the peak amplitude frequency, R_4 and R_6, are equal in value, which means that the filter can easily be tuned to different resonant frequencies. Secondly, the addition of the third op-amp further reduces the open-loop gain required from the op-amps. With this circuit, the op-amps require an open-loop gain of only about $3Q$ at the resonant frequency. The tunability of this section is particularly useful and will be illustrated by an example.

Say we want the resonant frequency of the CW filter described in the previous section to be continuously adjustable between 500 Hz and 1 kHz; how can this be achieved? If the values of C_1 and C_2 are set first, the other component values can then be calculated. We will set these two capacitors to a preferred value, $0.22\,\mu\text{F}$. For a resonant frequency of 500 Hz, this is equivalent to setting the section impedance level to

$$Z = \frac{1}{2\pi f_r \times C_1} = \frac{1}{2 \times \pi \times 500 \times 0.22 \times 10^{-6}} = 1447\,\Omega$$

and for a resonant frequency of 1 kHz

$$Z = \frac{1}{2 \times \pi \times 1000 \times 0.22 \times 10^{-6}} = 723\,\Omega$$

These values of impedance level are therefore the extreme values for R_4 and R_6. Subtracting these values gives a difference of $724\,\Omega$. To obtain practical values for R_4 and R_6, we will use a $680\,\Omega$ resistor in series with a $1\,\text{k}\Omega$ potentiometer in each position, which will give a slightly greater than specified tuning range.

Since the desired Q of the circuit is 10, the normalized value of R_8 is $(3Q-1) = 29\,\Omega$. If all the resistors except R_4 and R_6 are scaled to $1\,\text{k}\Omega$, and R_4 and R_6 are formed by a fixed $680\,\Omega$ and a variable $1\,\text{k}\Omega$ resistor in series, the

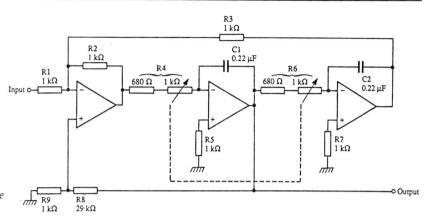

Figure 5.22 *The adjustable centre frequency CW band-pass filter*

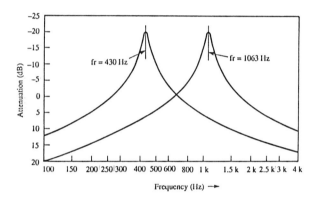

Figure 5.23 *Amplitude response of the adjustable centre frequency CW band-pass filter. An f_c of 430 Hz is obtained when the potentiometers are set to 1 k Ω, and an f_r of 1063 Hz is obtained when they are set to zero Ω.*

circuit shown in Fig. 5.22 results. Figure 5.23 shows the response of this circuit for the extreme settings of the potentiometers. When the potentiometers are set to 1 kΩ, a resonant frequency of about 430 Hz is obtained, and when set to zero, the resonant frequency is about 1063 Hz. The specified tuning range has therefore been slightly exceeded, as expected, because of the use of preferred values for the components forming R_4 and R_6. Because the band-pass Q of the section is 10, the gain at the resonant frequency for any setting of the potentiometers is 10 times, or 20 dB.

Wide-band band-pass filters

Wide-band, active band-pass filter requirements are best satisfied by cascading low-pass and high-pass filters. This approach was also used for wide-band passive band-pass filters, and the recommendation was given that a reasonable separation between the lower and upper cut-off frequencies should be maintained to minimize interaction between the low-pass and high-pass stages. It was also a requirement that the passive stages used should have identical impedances. These restrictions do not apply to active filters, because cascaded active stages are isolated from each other by the inherent properties of the op-amps.

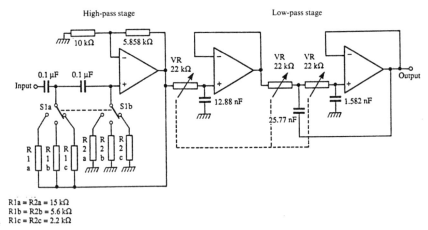

Figure 5.24 *A wide-band active filter with the lower cut-off frequency adjustable to nominally 100, 300 and 700 Hz and the upper cut-off frequency, continuously variable between about 2.5 kHz and 5 kHz*

Figure 5.25 *The amplitude response of the wide-band band-pass active filter showing two settings of the lower and upper cut-off frequencies, the outer response curve is obtained with the 15 kΩ setting of the high-pass section and the variable resistors in the low-pass stage set to about 5 kΩ. The inner response is obtained with the 2.2 kΩ and 20 kΩ settings respectively*

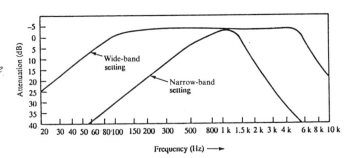

Since several active low-pass and high-pass filters have already been presented, this method of design will be illustrated with existing low-pass and high-pass designs. Figure 5.24 shows a band-pass filter formed by cascading the switchable cut-off frequency second-order Butterworth high-pass filter of Fig. 5.11 (b) and the variable cut-off frequency, third-order, 1 dB pass-band ripple Chebyshev low-pass filter first shown in Fig. 4.21. The input of the low-pass filter is driven directly by the output of the high-pass filter, with no worries about differing impedance levels.

Figure 5.25 shows the amplitude response of the complete filter. Responses for typical wide and narrow passband settings of the controls are shown. The performance of the low-pass and high-pass stages are as they were when used individually because of the inherent isolation of the active stages. The versatility of this circuit can be seen. It would be an extremely useful circuit to incorporate into the early audio stages of a receiver, allowing the audio band-width to be optimized to suit any modulation mode and set of listening conditions. In practice, it would be better to incorporate low-value resistors of, say, 1 kΩ in series with the 22 kΩ variable resistors in the low-pass stage so that these resistors cannot be set to 0 Ω. If a triple-gang potentiometer cannot be found or devised for use in the low-pass stage,

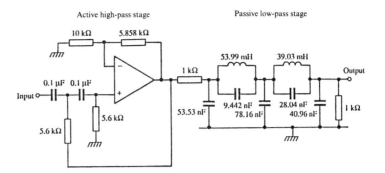

Figure 5.26 *A wide-band band-pass filter consisting of a 300 Hz second order Butterworth high-pass stage driving a 3.4 kHz passive low-pass elliptic filter based on CC05 20 47*

switches and various fixed resistors could be substituted, giving the choice of several useful upper cut-off frequencies.

The cascading approach to band-pass filter design is sufficiently general to allow active and passive filters to be cascaded. The circuit of Fig. 5.26 shows the Butterworth high-pass section used previously driving the fifth-order, elliptic, low-pass filter CC05 20 47, first shown in Fig. 2.27 (a). The high-pass filter has its cut-off frequency set to about 300 Hz, by choosing the frequency determining resistors to be 5.6 kΩ: if required, the switchable cut-off version could be used. The low-pass filter has its cut-off frequency scaled to 3.4 kHz and requires 1 kΩ driving and terminating impedances. Since the output impedance of the highpass section op-amp is very low, a 1 kΩ resistor is used to link the stages together to provide the correct drive impedance for the passive filter. Similarly, the low-pass filter is terminated by a 1 kΩ resistor on its output. The potentiometer action of these 1 kΩ resistors will produce an attenuation of 6 dB and this, coupled with the 4 dB gain of the active high-pass filter will produce an overall 2 dB of loss for the band-pass filter.

Active band-stop filters

Techniques are available for the design of active band-stop filters which allow narrow-band and wide-band filters to be obtained. Since active filters are mainly limited to audio frequencies, it is probably true that most applications for band-stop filters fall into the narrow-band category, the usual requirement being for a notch filter in the audio spectrum to remove an unwanted whistle.

Narrow-band band-stop filters

One interesting feature of narrow-band band-pass filter sections makes them useful in the design of band-stop filters: at the resonant frequency of the section, the phase shift of the output with respect to the input is precisely 0 or 180 degrees, depending on the exact implementation of the section. At resonance, the MFBP and state variable sections have phase shifts of 180 degrees, whereas the DABP section has a phase shift of 0 degrees. If the output of the band-pass section is summed with the original input signal, and account is taken of the phase shift at resonance and the gain of the section, it is possible

Figure 5.27 *The method of obtaining a narrow-band band-stop response by summing the output of a band-pass filter with the original signal to obtain cancellation at the band-pass filter resonant frequency*

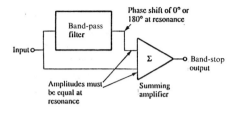

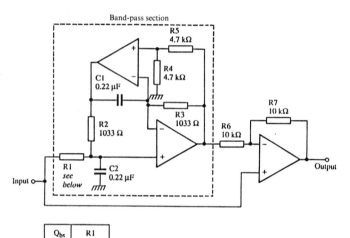

Figure 5.28 *Circuit diagram of a 700 Hz notch filter using the DABP band-pass section. Values for R_1 are shown for band-stop Q values of 3 and 5.*

Q_{bs}	R1
3	3099 Ω
5	5165 Ω

to obtain cancellation of the signals, giving a band-stop response. A block diagram demonstrating the technique is shown in Fig. 5.27.

Figure 5.28 shows the DABP band-stop circuit adapted into a 700 Hz notch filter with values of R_1 shown for band-stop Qs of 3 and 5. The band-pass section produces a peak gain of 2, and is non-inverting; so the input signal is summed into the non-inverting input of the summing block. A band-stop Q of 3 results in a 3 dB band-width of 233 Hz, compared with 140 Hz for a band-stop Q of 5. In theory, the notch at 700 Hz should be infinite in depth, the input signal being perfectly cancelled by its phase shifted counterpart. In practice, the degree of cancellation depends on how well the amplitudes of the signals presented to the summing amplifier match each other. By making R_6 a trimmer resistor, its exact value can be adjusted to give maximum depth to the notch.

A variable frequency notch filter

A useful band-stop filter would be one where the frequency of the notch could be varied over the audio range to eliminate an interfering tone, with the minimum effect on the rest of the audio spectrum. Such a filter is shown in Fig. 5.29, where a four-op-amp, state-variable section has been used to implement the band-pass phase-shifting stage. The values of C_1 and C_2, in association with the fixed and variable resistors used for R_4 and R_6, give a tuning range of approximately 300 Hz to 3.3 kHz, which should satisfy most requirements. With R_7 set to 200 Ω, the band-pass Q of the section is 5, giving the same value for the band-stop Q of the notch filter. A possible modification to the circuit would be to make R_7 variable, so that the band-stop Q of the filter could also be varied.

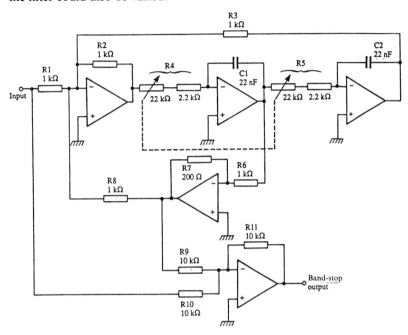

Figure 5.29 *The variable frequency notch filter with a band-stop Q of 5*

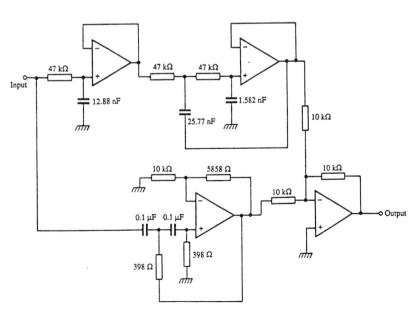

Figure 5.30 *Circuit diagram of a wide-band band-stop active filter, consisting of a 3rd order, 500 Hz cut-off frequency 1 dB pass-band ripple Chebyshev low-pass in parallel with a 2nd order, 4 kHz cut-off frequency Butterworth high-pass filter*

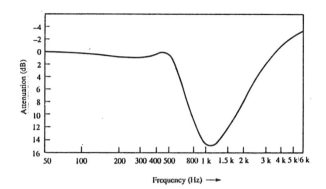

Figure 5.31 *Amplitude response of the wide-band band-stop filter*

Wide-band band-stop filters

Wide-band band-stop filters can be implemented by summing the outputs of low-pass and high-pass filters whose cut-off frequencies have been chosen to give the desired overall response. Fig. 5.30 shows the circuit of such a band-stop filter. The low-pass filter is the third-order, 1 dB pass band ripple Chebyshev filter of Fig. 4.17 (b) with its response-determining resistors adjusted to lower its cut-off frequency to approximately 500 Hz. The high-pass filter is the second-order Butterworth filter of Fig. 5.11 (b) modified for a cut-off frequency of 4 kHz. The resulting band-stop response is shown in Fig. 5.31. This circuit and its response are included here for completeness, showing that the technique is valid, although real applications for such responses are limited.

Summary and conclusions

A high-pass active filter can be obtained from a normalized low-pass proto-type by transforming the response-determining resistors into capacitors, the capacitors into resistors, and taking the reciprocal of the original component values. The resulting active high-pass filter is then scaled to the required cut-off frequency and impedance level in the same way as a low-pass active filter. Some active low-pass configurations have non-zero gain at DC and the low-pass to high-pass transformation results in this gain being achieved by the transformed high-pass filter as the frequency tends towards infinity. The values of d and ω_0, which determine the response of the filter, are incorporated into the low-pass prototype component values before transformation, exactly as they would be if the low-pass prototype was simply about to be scaled, and not transformed.

In most applications, the impedance level in an active section is less significant than in a passive filter, and so this illustrates one advantage that active filters have over passive designs. Another advantage is in the implementation of filters with variable cut-off frequencies, and a high-pass filter was described with switchable cut-off frequencies of nominally 100, 300 and 700 Hz.

Two methods of active band-pass filter design were described: using specifically designed band-pass sections, having controllable values of band-pass Q, and being most suitable for comparatively narrow-band applications; and cascading a low-pass and a high-pass filter to produce wider bandwidths.

A variety of band-pass sections were shown which simulate the behaviour of tuned circuits and are suitable for narrow-band applications. These ranged from the simple, multiple-feedback, single op-amp circuit to the multi op-amp, state-variable section, each having advantages and disadvantages when compared with each other. One particularly versatile circuit is the dual-amplifier band-pass (DABP) section, for which a variable band-pass Q filter example was shown. When a requirement for a variable-frequency band-pass filter was presented, the state-variable section was seen to be the best choice for its implementation.

Although the cascading technique is useful for producing wide-band active band-pass filters, it can be used for passband bandwidths which are much smaller than for passive filters. This is because the interaction between stages used in passive designs does not occur with active filters. Active and passive filters can also be cascaded, it being easier to position the output of the active filter driving the input of the passive filter, so that the low-impedance output of the active filter, in association with a series resistor, provides a well-defined drive impedance for the passive filter.

Two methods of active band-stop filter design were described: making use of the phase shift at resonance produced by narrow-band band-pass filters which, when summed with the original input signal, produces cancellation to give a narrow-band response; and connecting the inputs of a low-pass and a high-pass filter in parallel, summing the outputs to give a wide-band band-stop response.

The considerable range of low-pass, high-pass, band-pass and band-stop active filters described in this and the previous chapter should enable the designer to fulfil almost any audio frequency filtering requirement. Using a combination of these filters, a versatile audio processing unit could be built for use, for example, in a new receiver design, or as an add-on to an existing receiver. The variable cut-off frequencies and circuit Q values which can be implemented using active filters mean that the audio performance of such a unit can be optimized for any listening conditions.

6 Using real components

It is unfortunate that careful and accurate calculations performed during the design processes described in the previus chapters can be spoiled when a filter is built. Of course, this is not only true with filters, but applies to all electronic circuits: the effects of real components on filter performance seem to be one of the least understood areas of electronics. It is a commonly held view that filters are very intolerant of component variations and that highly accurate and expensive components must be used if acceptable results are to be obtained. This is not necessarily true and, in most cases, a gradual move away from the theoretical response will occur as components are appoximated towards their real properties, as is the case with many other circuits.

As a formal subject the study of the effects of component variations on the performance of a circuit is known as sensitivity and is highly mathematical. This is not the approach we shall take here. The approach we shall adopt is to use computer simulation to assess the effects of real components, the aim being to settle on designs which use off-the-shelf components needing no selection and filters which need no adjustment, for which the test equipment may not be available anyway.

One major advantage amateurs have over professionals when designing and building a filter is that the specification is usually fairly arbitrary and can be modified, to some extent, without seriously affecting the overall performance of the system into which the filter fits. Slight shifts in cut-off frequency, or an increase in passband ripple, may well be immaterial, especially if the benefit is a considerable reduction in the size and cost of the filter. What is needed is an appreciation of the properties of all the blocks in the system, so that the contribution of any degradation of the filter response towards the overall response can be assessed.

What are real components?

In the designs presented so far in this book, four types of components have been used: resistors, capacitors, inductors and op-amps. It has been assumed that these are ideal components, but what are the differences between these ideal components and the real components we can buy? These differences can broadly be summarized into three categories: real components are not available in an infinitely fine range of values; real components do not strictly obey the simple rules which are assumed for ideal components over an infinite range of frequencies; and real components have losses which are generally frequency-dependent.

One way of overcoming the first problem is to use series or parallel combinations of preferred-value components to build up the desired value. If, for example, a 1033 Ω resistor is called for in a design, it could be formed from a 1 kΩ and a 33 Ω resistor in series. What we are trying to achieve is to match the accuracy of the component with the resolution of the calculated value. This may be futile, since the 1033 Ω value is an approximation itself and may have been calculated originally to many decimal places on a calculator. It is therefore difficult to know where to stop with this approach. It would be much better if we knew that, if a component value varies within ±5% of its exactly the same argument can be put forward for other component types, In this way, we can be sure that if the accuracy of the component used in practice exceeds the tolerance for which the performance has been shown to be acceptable, then all will be well. It may turn out that a 1 kΩ resistor alone will produce perfectly acceptable results and so savings in the cost of the components used and the PCB area they occupy will be made.

Using a resistor value as an example may seem to be fairly trivial, but exactly the same argument can be put forward for other component types, such as capacitors and inductors. Capacitors are also available in ranges of values similar to those of resistors, but building up non-preferred values of capacitance from standard values results in bulky and expensive filters. Inductors cause even more headaches, as trying to obtain exact values will almost certainly necessitate winding a component by hand, with all the resulting inconvenience and expense. When the inductor has been wound, there may be little confidence that the inductance value is correct, unless measurement equipment is available.

Simple models for components, and our understanding of their operation, rely on straightforward rules or laws. We assume, for example, that op-amps have infinite open-loop gain and zero output impedace. The fact that we can successfully design and build circuits assuming these simple models is an indication that, in most cases, the models are sufficiently close to reality to make little difference. As long as we stay away from extremes of operating conditions for components, the simple models will be acceptable.

The component with which losses are most commonly associated is, of course, the inductor and the effect is most noticeable at low frequencies. We can fairly accurately model this effect by a resistor in series with the inductor, as will be shown later in this chapter. Capacitors can generally be assumed to be loss-free, and this is a reasonable assumption so long as the correct type of capacitor is chosen for the required frequency range of operation.

Passive audio filters

The problems of obtaining high-Q inductors for use in audio filters have, to some extent, been solved by W3NQN who has described many designs[1,2] using telephone-line loading coils, which are relatively high-Q components. Specialized designs have been developed which make use of the inductance

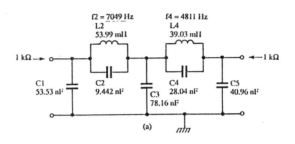

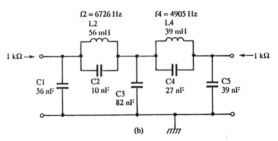

Figure 6.1 *CC05 20 47 scaled to 3.4 kHz, 1 k Ω*
a) has the exact component values,
b) has each component rounded to the nearest E12 preferred value

values offered by these coils, or by slight modifications to the inductors by removing turns. The result of using these telephone coils is a relatively bulky filter, but still worthwhile when the performance of such a filter is considered. This section is intended to help designers who cannot obtain these coils, or who would like to build more compact passive audio filters.

Figure 6.1 (a) shows the scaled version of CC05 20, 47, first shown in Fig. 2.27 (a). As the circuit stands, it is not straightforward to implement, the inductors needing to be wound on pot cores such as those manufactured by Mullard or Siemens, and each capacitor value made up of perhaps two capacitors in parallel to give a fairly close approximation to the values shown. Fig. 6.1(b) shows the same filter with all its components rounded to the nearest E12 preferred value. If acceptable results can be obtained with these values, the construction is considerably simplified, only a single capacitor being required for each capacitance and, as will be seen later, enabling off-the-shelf inductors to be used.

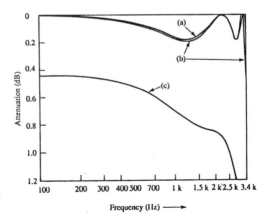

Figure 6.2 *Simulated amplitude response of CC05 20 47 scaled to 3.4 kHz cut-off frequency*
a) with exact values and ideal inductors
b) with rounded values and ideal inductors
c) with rounded values and real inductors
The response from 100–3400 Hz is shown

Curve (a) on Fig. 6.2 shows the simulated passband amplitude response of the filter with exact component values and curve (b) shows the response of the filter with rounded values. Only a very small deviation from the exact components response can be detected, indicated by a slight increase in the passband ripple from 0.18 dB to 0.2 dB and a marginal decrease in the ripple cut-off frequency. Fig. 6.3 shows the stopband response of these two versions of this filter. Again, curve (a) is the exact components response and

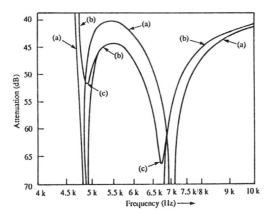

Figure 6.3 *Simulated stopband amplitude response of CC05 20 47 scaled to 3.4 kHz cut-off frequency*
a) with exact values and ideal inductors
b) with rounded values and ideal inductors
c) with rounded values and real inductors

Table 6.1 *Details of the Toko 10RB range of inductors*

INDUCTANCE (mH)	DC RESISTANCE (Ω)
1.0	3.4
1.2	3.7
1.5	4.0
1.8	4.5
2.2	5.2
2.7	5.8
3.3	6.1
3.9	7.2
4.7	7.5
5.6	8.4
6.8	9.7
8.2	10
10	12
12	13
15	15
18	17
22	19
27	22
33	26
39	45
47	52
56	58
68	66
82	71
100	82
120	97

Table 6.2 *Details of the Toko 10RBH range of inductors*

INDUCTANCE (mH)	DC RESISTANCE (Ω)
150	75
220	95
270	105
330	125
390	140
470	190
560	215
680	250
820	265
1000	295
1200	385
1500	435

curve (b) is the rounded values response. From curve (a), the two frequencies of infinite attenuation at 4811 Hz and 7049 Hz (being the resonant frequencies of L_4/C_4 and L_2/C_2 respectively) and the minimum stopband attenuation of 40 dB can be seen. When curve (b) is examined, there has been a slight shift in the frequencies of infinite attenuation to 4905 Hz and 6726 Hz, because of the change in the values of L_4/C_4 and L_2/C_2. Between these two frequencies, the minimum attenuation achieved is about 44 dB, better than the exact values response, and beyond 10 kHz the response tends towards the exact components response. In total, therefore, using rounded component values for this design results in very little significant change in the filter response.

Obviously, preferred value capacitors are easily and cheaply available. As far as the author is aware, the only inexpensive preferred-value inductors available in the UK are the 10 RB and 10 RBH ranges manufactured by Toko. Tables 6.1 and 6.2 show the inductance values available and the corresponding resistances of these inductors. Being only 14 mm high and 10.5 mm in diameter, they are ideally suited to printed-circuit-board mounting in compact modern equipment. The total range of values, from 1 mH to 1.5 H, suits the requirements for audio filters well and the only potential drawback of these components is their relatively low Q at audio frequencies. The Q of an inductor is given by

$$Q = \frac{2\pi f \times L}{R} \tag{6.1}$$

where f is the frequency at which the Q is calculated,
   L is the inductance,
   R is the resistance of the inductor.

Taking the 10RB 47 mH inductor as an example, its resistance is 52 Ω and so, at 1 kHz

$$Q = \frac{2\pi 1000 \times 47 \times 10^{-3}}{52} = 5.68$$

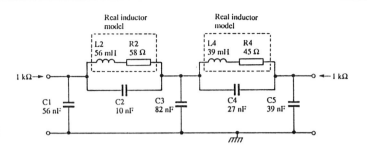

Figure 6.4 *The rounded value version of CC05 20 47 with resistors added in series with the inductors to simulate their finite Q*

Examination of a 47 mH inductor after removing its outer ferrite casing reveals a wire size of approximately 40 s.w.g. The Q of an inductor wound by hand on a ferrite core depends on the wire used, but the practical problems of handling the wire would necessitate using wire somewhat thicker than 40 s.w.g., giving a rather higher Q for the hand-wound component.

Figure 6.4 shows the rounded value version of CC05 20 47 with resistors added in series with each inductor to represent their DC resistance. Curve (c) in Figs. 6.2 and 6.3 shows the amplitude response now obtained. The filter exhibits non-zero loss at all frequencies (having a value of about 0.42 dB at 100 Hz) and increased passband ripple. Other effects of the low-Q inductors are the smoothing of the final passband ripple and a more gradual transition from the passband into the transition band. The frequencies of high attenuation in the stopband are indistinguishable from those obtained with the rounded values, ideal inductors response (curve (b)), but the attenuations are no longer infinite. They are approximately 52 dB at 4905 Hz and 66 dB at 6726 Hz. The minimum stopband attenuation is similar to that shown by curve (b). Practical results obtained from real filters indicate close agreement with these simulated results.

Flattening the response of the elliptic low-pass filter

If an application demands a flatter passband response than can be obtained with the filter of Fig. 6.4, but low-Q inductors are still to be used, some flattening of the response can be obtained at low frequencies by driving the filter via a capacitor. As was shown in Chapter 3, a series-connected capacitor can exhibit high-pass filtering characteristics.

When a capacitor is connected in series with a low-pass filter, as shown in Fig. 6.5, a band-pass filter is formed and the value of the capacitor can be chosen to have beneficial effects on the passband response of the original low-pass filter. If the response of the real components version of CC05 20 47 (Fig. 6.4) is simulated with various values of high-pass capacitor C, the

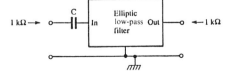

Figure 6.5 *An elliptic low-pass filter having a high-pass capacitor in series with its input to improve the passband flatness*

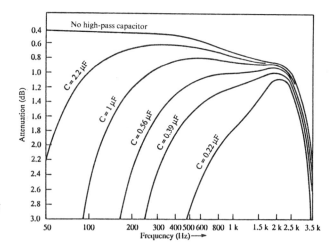

Figure 6.6 *Simulated amplitude response of CC05 20 47 scaled to 3.4 kHz cut-off frequency showing the effect of different high-pass capacitor values*

curves shown in Fig. 6.6 are produced. Low values of C give high attenuation at low frequencies, and progressively higher values of C give responses gradually tending towards the original low-pass response. One particularly useful value of C is $1\,\mu F$, which produces a significant decrease in the pass-band ripple compared to the unmodified response. No great increase in attenuation at 100 Hz occurs, but a useful 6 dB of attenuation at 50 Hz is produced, which helps to reduce mains hum in the audio path.

Another way of improving the response of a filter built with low-Q inductors is by incorporating an attenuation equalizer into the signal path. An attenuation equalizer is a network designed to modify the response of the original filter in the frequency range where the droop was most serious, that is, close to cut-off. The design of these equalizers is fairly straightforward and more information can be found in references 3 and 4.

High-pass audio filters

Figure 6.7 (a) shows the transformed Butterworth high-pass filter, originally

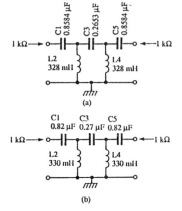

Figure 6.7 *The transformed high-pass filter scaled to 300 Hz, 1 k Ω:*
a) has the exact component values
b) has each component rounded to the nearest E12 preferred value

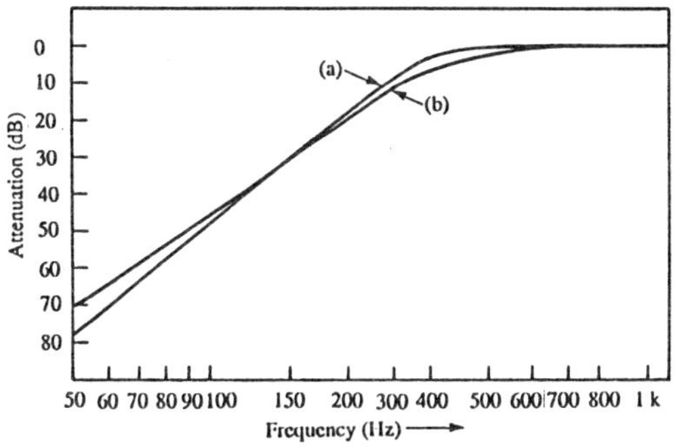

Figure 6.8 *Simulated amplitude response of the 5th order Butterworth high-pass filter*
a) with exact or rounded values and ideal inductors
b) with rounded values and real inductors

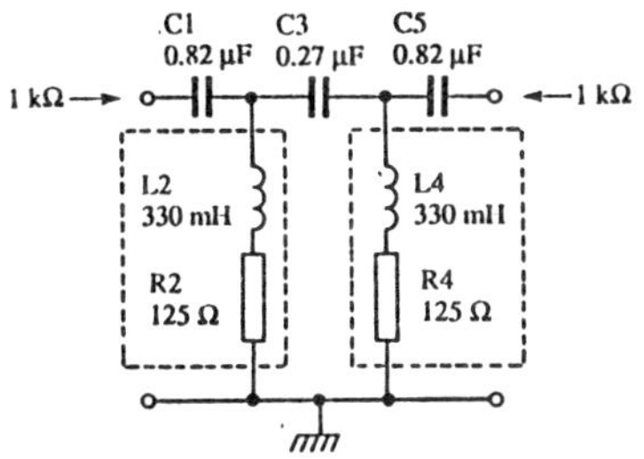

Figure 6.9 *The rounded value version of the high-pass filter with resistors added in series with the inductors to simulate their finite Q.*

Figure 6.10 *The 300 Hz–3.4 kHz audio band-pass filter with rounded values*
The 330 mH inductors are Toko 10 RBH
and the 56 mH and 39 mH inductors are Toko 10 RB

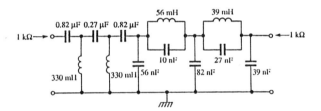

shown in Fig. 3.9 (b), and a rounded-components version is shown in Fig. 6.7 (b). The amplitude responses of these two filters is shown as curve (a) in Fig. 6.8. The responses are so nearly equal that they cannot be shown separately on this diagram, there being less than 1 dB difference between the responses at any frequency. When real inductors are substituted for L_2 and L_4, the circuit of Fig. 6.9 results, with the resistance of the 330 mH 10RBH Toko inductors represented by 125 Ω resistors R_2 and R_4. The response now obtained is curve (b) on Fig. 6.8. Rounding of the response near to the theoretical cut-off frequency is evident, as is a slight reduction in the stopband attenuation. The filter is still very useful and Fig. 6.10 shows it cascaded with the real-components version of CC05 20 47 to produce a practical audio band-pass filter.

Figure 6.11 shows the overall response of this band-pass filter (curve (b)), with the ideal-components response (curve (a)) shown for comparison. Curve (b) shows that the band-pass response is the sum of the low-pass and high-pass responses, and a thoroughly useful audio band-pass filter is produced.

Figure 6.11 *Simulated amplitude response of the cascaded Butterworth high-pass and elliptic low-pass audio filters shown in Fig. 6.10*
a) is the ideal components response
b) is the real components response

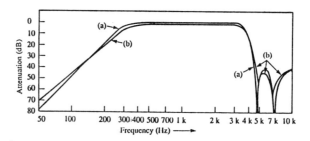

The significance of passband ripple

One notable effect on the performance of a filter using rounded components and low-Q inductors is an increase in passband ripple. Taking the version of CC05 20 47 using Toko inductors and preferred-value capacitors, we see almost 0.5 dB of ripple between 100 Hz and 2.5 kHz, compared to the theoretical value of 0.18 dB up to 3.4 kHz. The question has to be asked, therefore, whether this is a significant effect in practice for a filter used in, say, a receiver. We will try to answer this by looking for other sources of audio ripple and assessing what amplitude this ripple might be.

The first element which may introduce significant ripple is the IF filter. Although these filters are of a high quality, and are relatively expensive, they have a passband ripple of typically 1–3 dB. This ripple can effectively be doubled if you are communicating with someone using the same model of transceiver, since the peaks in ripple produced in the other station's transmit IF filter could correspond to the peaks in your receive IF filter, and vice versa.

Probably the biggest source of ripple in a receiver is the loudspeaker, which inherently has a non-linear electrical power input to sound pressure output characteristic. Typically, a 4-inch loudspeaker in free air exhibits 9 dB of riple from 1 kHz to 3 kHz in its sound pressure output[5]. When mounted in a metal case, with numerous cavities formed by metal dividers and printed-circuit boards around it, its frequency response is very unpredictable.

Another source of ripple is the response of the human ear. Experiments performed to measure the thresholds of audibility for pure tones[6] indicate that the ear exhibits typically 8 dB variation in the range 1 kHz to 3 kHz, being more sensitive at higher frequencies. Listeners to audio signals could therefore report quite different impressions when comparing the amplitudes of different frequencies.

These effects can negate attempts to minimize the passband ripple of audio filters. In this context, it would seem that the passband ripple found in the real-components elliptic filter described here is insignificant for most practical applications. Since, in many cases, increased passband ripple can be traded for rapid roll-off and/or greater stopband attenuation, advantage should be taken of the relative insignificance of passband ripple. This trade-off can be seen from Fig. 6.12, in which curves of minimum stopband attenuation are plotted against normalized start-of-stopband frequency for fifth-

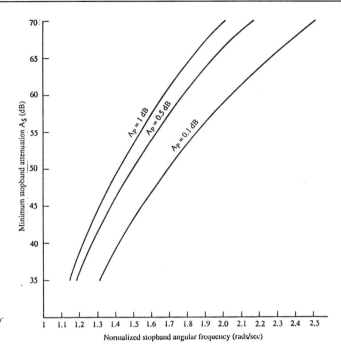

Figure 6.12 *Graphs of minimum stopband attentuation versus normalized stopband angular frequency of 5th order branch elliptic filters for various values of pass-band ripple (A_p)*

order elliptic filters of 0.1, 0.5 and 1 dB passband ripple. For a normalized stopband angular frequency of 1.5 rad/s an extra 10 dB of stopband attenuation can be obtained by using the 1 dB rather than the 0.1 dB filter. Alternatively, the 50 dB attenuation value can be achieved at 1.42 rad/s rather than at 1.7 rad/s by using the 1 dB filter. Another approach is to use a lower-order filter with a high-amplitude of ripple for a given application to achieve a stopband performance comparable to a higher-order filter with less ripple, thereby saving components and cost.

Driving and terminating passive audio filters

Whether passive audio filters are incorporated into existing equipment or included in new designs, correct source and termination impedances should be provided if predictable results are to be obtained. Fig. 6.13–6.16 show some methods commonly used to interface to these filters.

Figure 6.13 shows a common-emitter amplifier: the output impedance of this amplifier is effectively equal to the collector resistor R_s, which should be chosen to be equal to the source impedance of the filter. The base and emitter resistors for TR_1 should be chosen to set the DC voltage at its collector to a value that allows an AC swing compatible with the signal level being handled without the possibility of clipping. The output buffer amplifier, TR_2, is configured as an emitter follower, so the input impedance for the transistor itself is very high and the termination seen by the filter is the parallel combination of R_1 and R_2. Resistances R_1 and R_2 should therefore be chosen to terminate

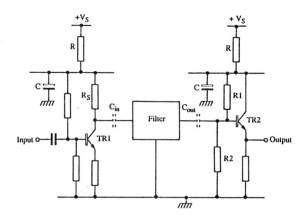

Figure 6.13 *Bipolar transistors driving and terminating an audio filter*

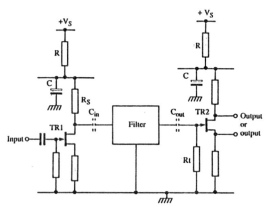

Figure 6.14 *Fets driving and terminating an audio filter*

the filter correctly and to set the DC operating conditions of TR_2. If a DC path exists from the input of the filter to ground or to the output, then the DC blocking capacitor, C_{in}, will be required. Similarly, if a DC path exists from the output of the filter to ground, then C_{out} will be required. The *RC* networks in the supply lines prevent any signal coupling from input to output via the rail, which would degrade the filter performance.

Figure 6.14 shows a circuit using fets for the driving and terminating devices. As in the bipolar transistor case, the source resistor of TR_1 provides the drive impedance to the filter, and the filter is terminated by the gate resistor of TR_2. Decoupling of the supply rails to the driving and terminating devices and DC isolation of the input and output of the filter are implemented as before.

Figure 6.15 shows an op-amp circuit. Because the output impedance of an op-amp with feedback is very low, the source impedance for the filter must be provided by a resistor, R_s. The termination is provided by R_t, the op-amp end of which is connected to ground as far as the filter is concerned. The feedback resistors for the op-amps can be chosen to provide any reasonable value of gain for these stages.

Often, the simplest way of adding an audio filter is in the low-impedance headphone output of a receiver. This is where passive filters have a consider-

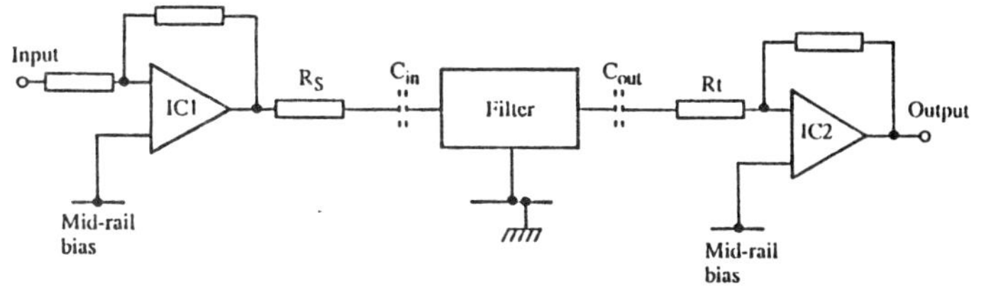

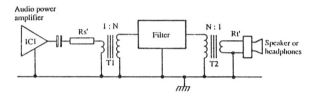

Figure 6.15 *Operational amplifiers driving and terminating an audio filter*

Figure 6.16 *Transformer coupled filter in audio output path*

able advantage over active filters because no power source is required, which can be a distinct problem to provide. A method used to couple the comparatively high impedance of the filter to the much lower impedance audio output of a receiver is shown in Fig. 6.16. Transformers T_1 and T_2 have a turns ratio equal to the square root of the ratio of the filter and speaker or headphones impedances. The output impedance of an audio power amplifier is very low (typically less than 1 Ω) and so there is a possibility that the input of the filter will be mismatched. This can be alleviated to some extent by incorporating a low value resistor, Rs' in series with the low-impedance drive to T_1 which will be transformed up to give a better match. Some loss in output level will result, but this can be compensated for by turning up the receiver volume level.

Of course, these driving and terminating techniques can be combined, and the final configuration chosen to make best use of available components.

Plate 6.1 shows a cascaded audio band-pass filter similar to that of Fig. 6.10 and a fifth-order elliptic low-pass filter side by side. On both PCBs, the filter components have been laid out in a straight line, keeping the outputs well away from the inputs, to reduce the chances of leakage around the filters. These filters would make excellent post-detector filters in high-quality superhet or direct-conversion SSB receivers, or band-limiting filters at the input to SSB transmitter modulators.

Plate 6.1

Radio-frequency filters

It has been shown that audio-frequency filters with acceptable responses can be built easily and cheaply by rounding the component values and using off-the-shelf inductors, but can this approach be extended to RF filters? Fig. 6.17 (a) shows the 2.2 MHz, 50 Ω version of C07 45, first shown in Fig. 2.29 (a), with exact component values. The passband and transition/stopband responses of this filter are shown as curve (a) on Figs. 6.18 and 6.19. When the components are rounded to their nearest E12 values, the circuit of Fig. 6.17 (b) is obtained. Curve (b) on Figs. 6.18 and 6.19 show the amplitude response of this circuit. The effect on the response has been minimal, consisting of a slight change in the passband ripple, which is most noticeable at the final trough close to cut-off and a slight shift in the ripple cut-off frequency. The transition/stopband response is better than that obtained originally, having greater attenuation at all frequencies.

As well as manufacturing the 10RB and 10RHB range of inductors, Toko also make a range of preferred-value RF inductors. The range considered here is the 7BS series, whose values and corresponding DC resistance are shown in Table 6.3. If 7BS inductors are used for the 3.9 μH components in Fig. 6.17 (b), DC resistances of 1 Ω have to be added in series with L_2, L_4 and L_6 to enable the real filter response to be simulated. The modified circuit is

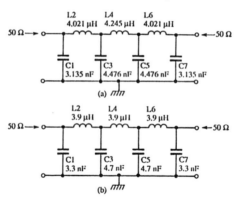

Figure 6.17 *C07 45 scaled to 2.2 MHz, 50 Ω:*
a) has the exact component values
b) has each component rounded to the nearest E12 preferred value

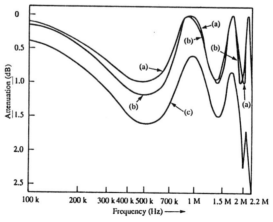

Figure 6.18 *Simulated passband amplitude response of C07 45 scaled to 2.2 MHz ripple cut-off frequency*
a) with exact values and ideal inductors
b) with rounded values and ideal inductors
c) with rounded values and real inductors

Table 6.3 *Details of the Toko 7BS range of inductors*

INDUCTANCE (uH)	DC RESISTANCE (ohm)
1.0	1.0
1.2	1.0
1.5	1.0
1.8	1.0
2.2	1.0
2.7	1.0
3.3	1.0
3.9	1.0
4.7	1.5
5.6	1.5
6.8	1.5
8.2	1.5
10	2.0
12	2.0
15	2.0
18	2.0
22	2.0
27	2.5
33	2.5
39	2.5
47	3.0
56	3.0
68	3.0
82	4.0
100	4.0
120	4.0
150	4.0
180	6.0
220	6.0
270	6.0
330	6.0
390	9.0
470	9.0
560	10
680	12
820	12
1000	14

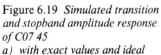

Figure 6.19 *Simulated transition and stopband amplitude response of C07 45*
a) with exact values and ideal inductors
b) with rounded values and ideal inductors
c) with rounded values and real inductors

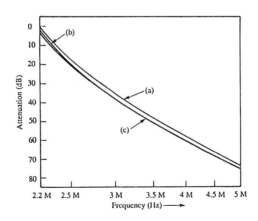

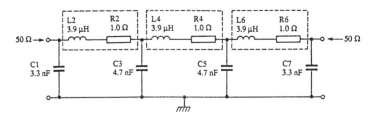

Figure 6.20 *The rounded value version of C07 45 with 1 Ω resistors added in series with the inductors to simulate their finite Q*

shown in Fig. 6.20. At 2.2 MHz (the nominal cut-off frequency of this filter) the Q of the 3.9 μH inductor is

$$Q = \frac{2\pi \times 2.2 \times 10^6 \times 3.9 \times 10^{-6}}{1.0} = 53.9$$

This is considerably higher than the Q of the 10RB and 10RBH inductors at audio frequencies. We should therefore expect less detrimental effects on the filter response when using these 7BS inductors.

Curve (c) on Figs. 6.18 and 6.19 shows the simulated response of the filter with real inductors. There is a finite loss at all frequencies and an increase in passband ripple, and the final ripple has been almost totally smoothed out. In the transition/stopband the filter behaves almost identically to the rounded-values, ideal-components circuit. For most applications, the response would be acceptable, particularly if care is taken to increase the nominal cut-off frequency before rounding so that any decreases in the cut-off frequency produced by using real components does not result in greater than acceptable attentuation just below the specified cut-off frequency.

The use of 7BS inductors allows high-pass, as well as low-pass, RF filters to be built easily and cheaply without the need for winding inductors, tuning coils or selecting capacitors. To show the versatility of this technique, a set of broadband RF filters will now be described.

Wide-band RF filters

One method described in Chapter 3 for the design of wide-band band-pass filters was to cascade low-pass and high-pass filters. The method will be illustrated here by the design of a set of filters suitable for the front end of a general-coverage receiver tuning the range 150 kHz to 30 MHz. It is possible to use a single band-pass filter with lower and upper cut-off frequencies of 150 kHz and 30 MHz, but it is desirable to use several filters, each covering a portion of the total tuning range so that the amount of RF energy reaching the first mixer of the receiver is considerably less than if a single filter is used.

The total tuning range therefore needs to be divided into several smaller bands. If we take 1 MHz to be the start frequency of one range and proceed in one-octave steps, we obtain the following bands: 1–2 MHz, 2–4 MHz, 4–8 MHz, 8–16 MHz and 16–30 MHz. This leaves 150 kHz to 1 MHz as the sixth band which, although it is greater than one octave, is reasonable to cover in one band. This, or one very similar, is a commonly found set of front-end filter bands in many commercially available receivers and transceivers. The use of this type of filter has implications in the choice of interme-

Table 6.4 *Frequency coverage of the wide-band filters*

FILTER NUMBER	FREQUENCY COVERAGE
1	0.135–1.1MHz
2	0.9–2.2MHz
3	1.8–4.4MHz
4	3.6–8.8MHz
5	7.2–17.6MHz
6	14.4–33.0MHz

diate frequency for such a receiver. To avoid image rejection and IF breakthrough problems, the first IF must be well outside the 150 kHz to 30 MHz range covered, and preferably be at VHF frequencies such as 70 MHz or higher.

Since the aim is to use preferred-value capacitors and inductors to build these filters, the nominal bands to be covered by each filter will be extended by 10% at the lower and upper cut-off frequencies to allow for component tolerance, giving the coverages shown in Table 6.4. The starting point when designing these filters is to select a suitable normalized low-pass filter for use both as a scaled low-pass filter and as a prototype for transformation to a high-pass filter. The prototype chosen is C07 25, a 7-pole, 0.28 dB passband ripple Chebyshev design, which has a theoretical attenuation of 62 dB at twice the cut-off frequency (compared with 42 dB for a Butterworth filter of the same complexity) and 89 dB at three times the cut-off frequency.

There are, of course, two circuit configurations for a 7-pole Chebyshev low-pass filter: the minimum inductor and the minimum capacitor implementations. The normalized component values for the two implementations are the same, with L_1 in the minimum-inductor design having the same value as C_1 in the minimum-capacitor design, and so on. If we want to use the minimum total number of inductors in the final design, we should use the minimum-inductor version as the prototype for the scaled low-pass section and the minimum-capacitor version as the prototype for the high-pass transformation. However, as will be seen later, it can be advantageous to use a minimum-capacitor high-pass section when electronically-switched filters are required.

Since the frequency coverage of the filters has been decided, it is only necessary now to decide on the input and output impedance, so that the practical designs can be produced. It is not necessarily the best approach simply to look at the impedance of the antenna system and design the filters to match it directly. When filters which are easy to implement are required, we must look at the component values obtained when various filter impedance options are considered. Table 6.5 shows the 1 Ω, 1 rad/s component values for the low-pass prototype and the values obtained when they are

Table 6.5 *Component values of the 7 pole 0.28 dB Chebyshev minimum inductor low-pass filters showing the effect of different input/output impedances*

COMPONENT	1 1 rad/s VALUE	50 1.1MHz VALUE	450 1.1MHz VALUE	50 33MHz VALUE	450 33MHz VALUE
C1	1.488F	4.306nF	478.4pF	143.5pF	15.95pF
C3	2.388F	6.910nF	767.8pF	230.3pF	25.59pF
C5	2.388F	6.910nF	767.8pF	230.3pF	25.59pF
C7	1.488F	4.306nF	478.4pF	143.5pF	15.95pF
L2	1.343H	9.716uH	87.44uH	0.3239uH	2.915uH
L4	1.451H	10.50uH	94.47uH	0.3499uH	3.149uH
L6	1.343H	9.716uH	87.44uH	0.3239uH	2.915uH

scaled to 1.1 MHz and 33 MHz cut-off frequencies for two different impedances, $50\,\Omega$ and $450\,\Omega$. Since the ratio of $450\,\Omega$ to $50\,\Omega$ is nine, the $50\,\Omega$ capacitors are nine times larger than the $450\,\Omega$ capacitors, and the $50\,\Omega$ inductors are nine times smaller than the $450\,\Omega$ inductors. The result is that the inductors for the $50\,\Omega$, 33 MHz filter have values which are less than $1\,\mu H$, which is the lower limit for the Toko 7BS range of inductors. Because the aim is to produce designs which use these inductors, the designs presented here will have $450\,\Omega$ input and output impedances, and details will be given later of how $50\,\Omega$ and $75\,\Omega$ antennas can be used with these designs.

In Table 6.6, component values for the six filters with the desired upper cut-off frequencies are shown. The exact values are given, along with the nearest E12 value. It can be seen that the smallest inductor value (for L_2 and L_6 in the $450\,\Omega$, 33 MHz design) is $2.915\,\mu H$ (rounded to $2.7\,\mu H$) and all the inductors can be selected from the 7BS range.

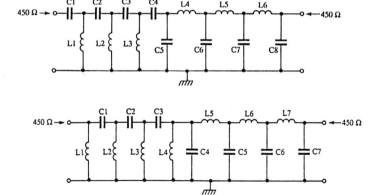

Figure 6.21 *Circuit diagram of cascaded high-pass and low-pass filters. Minimum inductor high-pass filter is used in this implementation*

Figure 6.22 *Circuit diagram of cascaded high-pass and low-pass filters. Minimum capacitor high-pass filter is used in this implementation*

Table 6.6 *Component values of 7 pole 0.28 dB Chebyshev minimum inductor low-pass filters.*

COMPONENT	1 ohm, 1 rad/sec VALUE	450 ohm, 1.1MHz VALUE	450 ohm, 2.2MHz VALUE	450 ohm, 4.4MHz VALUE	450 ohm, 8.8MHz VALUE	450 ohm, 17.6MHz VALUE	450 ohm, 33.0MHz VALUE
C1 EXACT	1.488F	478.4pF	239.2pF	119.6pF	59.80pF	29.90pF	15.95pF
C1 ROUNDED	-	470pF	220pF	120pF	56pF	27pF	15pF
C3 EXACT	2.388F	767.8pF	383.9pF	192.0pF	95.98pF	47.99pF	25.59pF
C3 ROUNDED	-	820pF	390pF	180pF	100pF	47pF	27pF
C5 EXACT	2.388F	767.8pF	383.9pF	192.0pF	95.98pF	47.99pF	25.59pF
C5 ROUNDED	-	820pF	390pF	180pF	100pF	47pF	27pF
C7 EXACT	1.488F	478.4pF	239.2pF	119.6pF	59.80pF	29.90pF	15.95pF
C7 ROUNDED	-	470pF	220pF	120pF	56pF	27pF	15pF
L2 EXACT	1.343H	87.44uH	43.72uH	21.86uH	10.93uH	5.465uH	2.915uH
L2 ROUNDED	-	82uH	47uH	22uH	10uH	5.6uH	2.7uH
L4 EXACT	1.451H	94.47uH	47.24uH	23.62uH	11.81uH	5.905uH	3.149uH
L4 ROUNDED	-	100uH	47uH	22uH	12uH	5.6uH	3.3uH
L6 EXACT	1.343H	87.44uH	43.72uH	21.86uH	10.93uH	5.465uH	2.915uH
L6 ROUNDED	-	82uH	47uH	22uH	10uH	5.6uH	2.7uH

Table 6.7 *Component values of 7 pole 0.28 dB Chebyshev minimum inductor high-pass filters*

LOWPASS PROTOTYPE COMPONENT	1 ohm, 1 rad/s VALUE	TRANSFORMED HIGHPASS COMPONENT	1 ohm, 1 rad/s VALUE	450 ohm, 0.133MHz VALUE	450 ohm, 0.9MHz VALUE	450 ohm, 1.8MHz VALUE	450 ohm, 3.6MHz VALUE	450 ohm, 7.2MHz VALUE	450 ohm, 14.4MHz VALUE
L1	1.488H	C1 EXACT	0.672F	1761pF	264.1pF	132.0pF	66.02pF	33.01pF	16.50pF
		C1 ROUNDED	-	1800pF	270pF	120pF	68pF	33pF	15pF
L3	2.388H	C3 EXACT	0.419F	1098pF	164.7pF	82.33pF	41.16pF	20.58pF	10.29pF
		C3 ROUNDED	-	1000pF	150pF	82pF	39pF	22pF	10pF
L5	2.388H	C5 EXACT	0.419F	1098pF	164.7pF	82.33pF	41.16pF	20.58pF	10.29pF
		C5 ROUNDED	-	1000pF	150pF	82pF	39pF	22pF	10pF
L7	1.488H	C7 EXACT	0.672F	1761pF	264.1pF	132.0pF	66.02pF	33.01pF	16.50pF
		C7 ROUNDED	-	1800pF	270pF	120pF	68pF	33pF	15pF
C2	1.343H	L2 EXACT	0.745H	395.2uH	59.29uH	29.64uH	14.82uH	7.411uH	3.705uH
		L2 ROUNDED	-	390uH	56uH	27uH	15uH	6.8uH	3.9uH
C4	1.451H	L4 EXACT	0.689H	365.5uH	54.83uH	27.41uH	13.71uH	6.854uH	3.427uH
		L4 ROUNDED	-	390uH	56uH	27uH	15uH	6.8uH	3.3uH
C6	1.343H	L6 EXACT	0.745H	395.2uH	59.29uH	29.64uH	14.82uH	7.411uH	3.705uH
		L6 ROUNDED	-	390uH	56uH	27uH	15uH	6.8uH	3.9uH

Table 6.8 *Component values of 7 pole 0.28 dB Chebyshev minimum capacitor high-pass filters*

LOWPASS PROTOTYPE COMPONENT	1 ohm, 1 rad/s VALUE	TRANSFORMED HIGHPASS COMPONENT	1 ohm, 1 rad/s VALUE	450 ohm, 0.133MHz VALUE	450 ohm, 0.9MHz VALUE	450 ohm, 1.8MHz VALUE	450 ohm, 3.6MHz VALUE	450 ohm, 7.2MHz VALUE	450 ohm, 14.4MHz VALUE
C1	1.488F	L1 EXACT	0.672H	356.5uH	53.48uH	26.74uH	13.37uH	6.685uH	3.342uH
		L1 ROUNDED	–	330uH	56uH	27uH	15uH	6.8uH	3.3uH
C3	2.388F	L3 EXACT	0.419H	222.3uH	33.34uH	16.67uH	8.336uH	4.168uH	2.084uH
		L3 ROUNDED	–	220uH	33uH	18uH	8.2uH	3.9uH	2.2uH
C5	2.388F	L5 EXACT	0.419H	222.3uH	33.34uH	16.67uH	8.336uH	4.168uH	2.084uH
		L5 ROUNDED	–	220uH	33uH	18uH	8.2uH	3.9uH	2.2uH
C7	1.488F	L7 EXACT	0.672H	356.5uH	53.48uH	26.74uH	13.37uH	6.685uH	3.342uH
		L7 ROUNDED	–	330uH	56uH	27uH	15uH	6.8uH	3.3uH
L2	1.343H	C2 EXACT	0.745F	1952pF	292.8pF	146.4pF	73.19pF	36.60pF	18.30pF
		C2 ROUNDED	–	1800pF	270pF	150pF	68pF	39pF	18pF
L4	1.451H	C4 EXACT	0.689F	1805pF	270.8pF	135.4pF	67.69pF	33.84pF	16.92pF
		C4 ROUNDED	–	1800pF	270pF	150pF	68pF	33pF	18pF
L6	1.343H	C6 EXACT	0.745F	1952pF	292.8pF	146.4pF	73.19pF	36.60pF	18.30pF
		C6 ROUNDED	–	1800pF	270pF	150pF	68pF	39pF	18pF

Table 6.9 *Rounded component values of the band-pass filters shown in Fig. 6.21*

FREQUENCY (MHz)	C1 (pF)	L1 (uH)	C2 (pF)	L2 (uH)	C3 (pF)	L3 (uH)	C4 (pF)	C5 (pF)	L4 (uH)	C6 (pF)	L5 (uH)	C7 (pF)	L6 (uH)	C8 (pF)
0.135-1.1	1800	390	1000	390	1000	390	1800	470	82	820	100	820	82	470
0.9-2.2	270	56	150	56	150	56	270	220	47	390	47	390	47	220
1.8-4.4	120	27	82	27	82	27	120	120	22	180	22	180	22	120
3.6-8.8	68	15	39	15	39	15	68	56	10	100	12	100	10	56
7.2-17.6	33	6.8	22	6.8	22	6.8	33	27	5.6	47	5.6	47	5.6	27
14.4-33.0	15	3.9	10	3.3	10	3.9	15	15	2.7	27	3.3	27	2.7	15

Table 6.10 *Rounded component values of the band-pass filters shown in Fig. 6.22*

FREQUENCY (MHz)	L1 (uH)	C1 (pF)	L2 (uH)	C2 (pF)	L3 (uH)	C3 (pF)	L4 (uH)	C4 (pF)	L5 (uH)	C5 (pF)	L6 (uH)	C6 (pF)	L7 (uH)	C7 (pF)
0.135-1.1	330	1800	220	1800	220	1800	330	470	82	820	100	820	82	470
0.9-2.2	56	270	33	270	33	270	56	220	47	390	47	390	47	220
1.8-4.4	27	150	18	150	18	150	27	120	22	180	22	180	22	120
3.6-8.8	15	68	8.2	68	8.2	68	15	56	10	100	12	100	10	56
7.2-17.6	6.8	39	3.9	33	3.9	39	6.8	27	5.6	47	5.6	47	5.6	27
14.4-33.0	3.3	18	2.2	18	2.2	18	3.3	15	2.7	27	3.3	27	2.7	15

We now need to produce a range of high-pass filters and, to do this, the low-pass to high-pass transformation will be used. Table 6.7 shows the component values for the minimum-inductor high-pass filters for the six cut-off frequencies required. The highest (395.2 μH, rounded to 390 μH) and the lowest (3.427 μH, rounded to 3.3 μH) inductor values also fit conveniently into the Toko 7BS inductor range. Table 6.8 shows the component values for the minimum-capacitor high-pass filters and again all the scaled inductor values can be obtained in the Toko 7BS range.

Figures 6.21 and 6.22 show the low-pass and high-pass filters cascaded to form band-pass filters. A summary of the rounded-component values for these two configurations (obtained from Tables 6.6–6.8) are shown in Table 6.9 and 6.10. These designs are thoroughly practical computer simulations and experimental measurements have revealed passband ripple values of less than 2 dB and insertion losses of less than 1.5 dB.

Filter switching

The choice of the minimum-inductor or minimum-capacitor implementation for the high-pass sections can be based on the switching arrangement used for multi-band operation. Probably the simplest method is to use mechanical switches, switching the inputs and outputs of the filters on

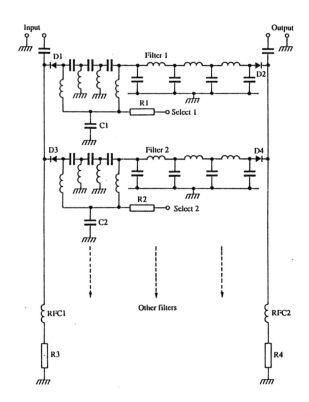

Figure 6.23 *Circuit diagram of electronically-switched wideband band-pass filters*

ganged sections. Care should be taken with the connections to and from the switches, keeping them as short and direct as possible and using screened cable if possible. This will help to reduce leakage around the filters due to radiation and pick-up in the connecting wires. PCB-mounted switches are available which simplify the production of compact, low-leakage multi-band arrangements.

Figure 6.23 shows an electronically switched bank of cascaded low-pass and high-pass filters using diodes such as BA244s as the switching elements. A filter is selected by applying a positive voltage (typically 12 volts) to the relevent SELECT line, while holding the other SELECT lines at zero volts. The advantage of using the minimum-capacitor implementation for the high-pass sections can now be seen: the current used to turn on the diodes is allowed to pass through two of the high-pass inductors. Consider, for example, a positive voltage applied to the SELECT1 line: current flows to ground through R_1, the first high-pass inductor, D_1, RFC_1 and R_3; current also flows through R_1, the final high-pass inductor, D_2 the low-pass inductors, RFC_2 and R_4. Diodes D_1 and D_2 are therefore forward biased and present low-impedance paths to RF signals, placing FILTER 1 in circuit. The diodes in series with the other filters are reversed biased, blocking the signal path. Chokes RFC_1 and RFC_2 are included to present high impedances to the input and output signals, preventing R_3 and R_4 from affecting the drive and termination impedances seen by the filter switched in circuit. The values of R_1, R_3 and R_4 are chosen to set the DC current through the diodes and only a few milliamps will be necessary. The earthy ends of the first and last high-pass inductors are decoupled to ground by capacitors, so the high-pass filter appears as the normal configuration to input signals, with the earthy end of all its inductors grounded.

The choice of frequency coverage for each of the wide-band filters described previously simplifies control of the filter switching. This occurs because filter selection can be based on the value of the tuned frequency in megahertz, without having to switch filters in the middle of any MHz segment. If a synthesized first local oscillator is used in the receiver, the MHz value of the tuned frequency, and hence the filter to be selected, can be derived from the data controlling the synthesizer.

Broad-band transformers

The use of $450\,\Omega$ as the input/output impedance of the wide-band filters solves some problems of implementation, but can be inconvenient if they are to be used with other than $450\,\Omega$ antennas, particularly ones with impedances as low as $50\,\Omega$ and $75\,\Omega$. What is required is a broad-band transformer, capable of performing an impedance transformation over the wide frequency range covered by these filters. Many designs of broad-band transformers have been published[7,8,9] but often lack practical details for specific applications. Toroidal cores are popular as the magnetic medium and several of these designs have been tried by the author without much success. By far the best, and the simplest, design tried so far is that used in the Micron trans-

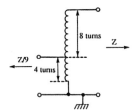

Figure 6.24 *Diagram of the 9 : 1 impedance transformer*

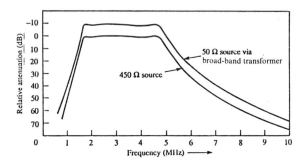

Figure 6.25 *Frequency response of the 1.8–4.4 MHz wideband filter, driven directly by 8 a 450 Ω source, and by a 50 Ω source via the broad-band transformer*

ceiver[10]. This is an auto-transformer wound on a Fair-rite two-hole core, type 28–43002402, requiring only 12 turns for a 9 : 1 impedance transformation. A diagram of this transformer is shown in Fig. 6.24.

To wind the transformer, about 30 cm of 0.2 mm (36 s.w.g.) enamelled wire is needed. Wind eight turns through the two holes of the core and then pass the long end of the wire back into one hole, leaving a loop of wire loose which will form the tap two-thirds down the winding. Complete the winding of the remaining four turns on the core. Mark the curved side of the core where the wire emerges on the last turn to identify the earthy end of the winding. Cut the loop of wire, trim all the ends to length, remove the insulation and twist the tap wires together. The transformer is now ready for soldering into a board.

The performance of the transformer can be seen from Fig. 6.25, where a 50 Ω source is driving the 1.8–4.4 MHz wide-band filter via the transformer. The response of the filter driven directly by a 450 Ω source is also plotted for comparison. The transormer gives a 9.5 dB (that is, 3 times) voltage increase as a result of the impedance change, as can be seen from the plots. All the wide-band filters described earlier have been tested with this transformer and in all cases good matches were obtained.

If a match to a 75 Ω antenna is required, a total of only 9.5 turns is needed for the transformer, with the tap still at four turns above ground. This gives the required impedance transformation of approximately 6 : 1.

Front-end attenuators

Because the use of broad-band, rather than narrow-band, front-end filters results in considerable unwanted RF energy reaching the RF amplifier or first mixer, receivers using them can be prone to overloading problems. This is why the large signal-handling performance of the first active stage of modern receivers is so important. One method of reducing the possibility of overloading is to provide the option of adding some attenuation into the signal path. This can be effective in improving reception both when the desired signal is strong and is causing overload effects and when a strong undesired signal is masking a weaker signal.

The simplest method of providing attenuation is to place a potentiometer between the antenna and the filters, which is adjusted to step down the input signal by a variable amount depending on the severity of overloading. However, this has two disadvantages: firstly, it is difficult to provide predictable and calibrated attenuation levels, and secondly, the front-end filters are likely to see different drive impedances depending on the setting of the attenuator potentiometer. These problems can be overcome by providing a range of constant-impedance attenuator networks which are switched into circuit as required, giving calibrated attenuations while still matching the filters.

Two simple configurations are available for unbalanced (that is, one side of the input and output is connected to ground) attenuators: symmetrical T-networks (shown in Fig. 6.26) and symmetrical pi-networks (see Fig. 6.27). For the T-networks, the values of the resistors are given by:

$$R_1 = Z \frac{1-k}{1+k} \tag{6.2}$$

$$R_2 = Z \frac{2k}{1-k^2} \tag{6.3}$$

where Z is the input/output impedance of the network,
k is the desired attenuation, expressed as a ratio.

For the pi-networks, the values of the resistors are given by

$$R_1 = Z \frac{1+k}{1-k} \tag{6.4}$$

$$R_2 = Z \frac{1-k^2}{2k} \tag{6.5}$$

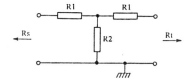

Figure 6.26 *Circuit diagram of symmetrical T-network attenuator*

Table 6.11 *Symmetrical T-network attenuator component values*

ATTENUATION (dB)	50 ohm IMPEDANCE				75 ohm IMPEDANCE				450 ohm IMPEDANCE			
	R1,R3 (ohm)		R2 (ohm)		R1,R3 (ohm)		R2 (ohm)		R1,R3 (ohm)		R2 (ohm)	
	EXACT	ROUNDED	EXACT	ROUNDED	EXACT	ROUNDED	EXACT	ROUNDED	EXACT	ROUNDED	EXACT	ROUNDED
5	14.0	15	82.2	82	21.0	22	123	120	126	120	740	680
10	26.0	27	35.1	33	39.0	39	52.7	56	234	220	316	330
15	34.9	33	18.4	18	52.4	56	27.5	27	314	330	165	150
20	40.9	39	10.1	10	61.4	56	15.2	15	368	390	90.9	82
25	44.7	47	5.64	5.6	67.0	68	8.46	8.2	402	390	50.8	47
30	46.9	47	3.17	3.3	70.4	68	4.74	4.7	422	390	28.5	27
35	48.3	47	1.78	1.8	72.4	68	2.67	2.7	434	470	16.0	15
40	49.0	47	1.00	1.0	73.5	68	1.50	1.5	441	470	9.0	8.2

Table 6.12 *Symmetrical pi-network attenuator component values*

ATTENUATION (dB)	50 ohm IMPEDANCE				75 ohm IMPEDANCE				450 ohm IMPEDANCE			
	R1,R3 (ohm)		R2 (ohm)		R1,R3 (ohm)		R2 (ohm)		R1,R3 (ohm)		R2 (ohm)	
	EXACT	ROUNDED	EXACT	ROUNDED	EXACT	ROUNDED	EXACT	ROUNDED	EXACT	ROUNDED	EXACT	ROUNDED
5	178	180	30.4	33	268	270	45.6	47	1606	1500	274	270
10	96.2	100	71.2	68	144	150	107	100	866	820	640	680
15	71.6	68	136	150	107	100	204	220	645	680	1225	1.2k
20	61.1	56	248	270	91.7	100	371	390	550	560	2228	2.2k
25	56.0	56	443	470	83.9	82	665	680	503	470	3988	3.9k
30	53.3	56	790	820	79.9	82	1185	1.2k	479	470	7108	6.8k
35	51.8	56	1405	1.5k	77.7	82	2108	2.2k	466	470	12649	12k
40	51.0	56	2500	2.7k	76.5	82	3750	3.9k	459	470	22498	22k

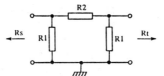

Figure 6.27 *Circuit diagram of symmetrical π-network attenuator*

Component values for several typical networks are shown in Tables 6.11 and 6.12. Attenuation levels from 5 dB to 40 dB (in steps of 5 dB) for impedances of 50 Ω, 75 Ω and 450 Ω are catered for in these tables, although resistor values for other attenuations and impedances can be calculated using the above equations. Rounded resistor values are given, as for the filter components, and these make very little practical difference to the performance of the attenuators themselves or the filters they drive.

The choice of attenuator type is a matter of personal preference. A useful set of attenuation values to incorporate into a receiver front end would be 10, 20 and 30 dB, with the option of switching the attenuators out of circuit altogether. It is hardly worthwhile building a PCB containing the attenuator resistors and making connections to a front panel switch. It is much easier to mount the resistors on the attenuator switch itself.

Narrow-band filters for the amateur bands

For an amateur bands only receiver, the best solution to the front-end filtering requirement is to use narrow-band filters. As well as reducing considerably the amount of unwanted RF energy reaching the first active stage, they also allow the use of a lower intermediate frequency in the receiver, simplifying the IF amplifier design. The easiest method of obtaining a narrow-band response is to use the tuned circuit approach, as described in Chapter 3. Table 6.13 shows the frequency coverage, the arithmetic centre frequency and the corresponding band-pass Q required of a narrow-band filter, for each of the nine amateur bands below 30 MHz. Because the band-pass Q values are comparatively high, it is valid to use the arithmetic, rather than the geometric, centre frequency without introducing any significant error. Ideally, it should be possible to design a filter for each band exactly matched to the band-width and centre frequency requirement for that band, giving rejection of unwanted signals immediately outside the band. The approach taken here will be to use easily available Toko inductors which make construction easy, even for the relatively inexperienced constructor, but which inevitably demand some compromise in the band-width obtained.

In Chapter 3 it was seen that a shunt-connected tuned circuit acts as a band-pass filter and that the sharpness of the peak obtained in its amplitude response (quantified by its band-pass Q) depends on the driving and terminating impedances. To obtain greater band-pass Q values, two or more filters can be cascaded, each contributing to the roll-off rate away from resonance.

The circuit of a basic practical narrow-band filter is shown in Fig. 6.28.

Table 6.13 *Values of circuit Q required for ideal band-pass filters for the amateur bands below 30 MHz*

BAND (MHz)	CENTRE FREQUENCY (MHz)	BANDPASS Q
1.8–2.0	1.9	9.5
3.5–3.8	3.65	12.2
7.0–7.1	7.05	70.5
10.1–10.15	10.125	202.5
14.0–14.35	14.175	40.5
18.07–18.17	18.12	181.2
21.0–21.45	21.225	47.2
24.89–24.99	24.94	249.4
28.0–29.7	28.85	41.2

This consists of two tuned circuits, capacitively coupled and linked to the input and output terminals via low-impedance windings on transformers. The effect of using this arrangement for the input and output connections is to transform upwards the impedance seen by the tuned circuits, enabling sharper responses to be obtained even with low impedance antennas. Table 6.14 shows the component values chosen for these filters. Three types of transformer are used: Toko 10K types KANK3333, KANK3334 and KANK3335, which have nominal secondary inductances of $45\,\mu$H, $5.5\,\mu$H and $1.2\,\mu$H respectively. The inductance of these transformers can be adjusted by about 30% by rotating the slug cores fitted. Capacitors C_1 and C_3 are calculated to resonate the inductor secondaries at the centre of each band by adjusting the cores of T_1 and T_2. The value of C_2 is critical to the filter performances, since it sets the coupling between the two tuned circuits. When these types of tuned circuits are used in oscillators, the effects of temperature variations on the resonant frequency can be critical. However, this will not be a problem when using them in filters.

The effect that varying C_2 has on a filter response is shown in Fig. 6.29. Here, the 14 MHz filter response has been plotted for three different values of C_2. With $C_2 = 2.2$pF, the insertion loss of the filter is approximately 4 dB, this is

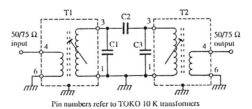

Figure 6.28 *Circuit diagram of the two tuned circuit narrow-band filter*

Pin numbers refer to TOKO 10 K transformers

Table .14 *Component values of the 2 tuned circuit narrow-band filters for 50 and 75 Ω input/output impedances*

BAND (MHz)	T1,T2 TYPE	C1,C3 (pF)	C2 (pF) 50 ohm	C2 (pF) 75 ohm
1.8–2.0	3333	150	12	8.2
3.5–3.8	3333	39	3.3	3.3
7.0–7.1	3334	100	8.2	8.2
10.1–10.15	3334	47	6.8	3.3
14.0–14.35	3334	22	3.3	3.3
18.07–18.17	3335	68	6.8	3.3
21.0–21.45	3335	47	4.7	3.3
24.89–24.99	3335	33	3.3	3.3
28.0–29.7	3335	22	3.3	3.3

Key to transformer types:

```
3333: KANK3333R (45uH)  Toko 10K
3334: KANK3334R (5.5uH) Toko 10K
3335: KANK3335R (1.2uH) Toko 10K
```

the undercoupled case; with $C_2 = 6.8\,\text{pF}$, a single peak in the response cannot be obtained, not because of de-tuning but because the two tuned circuits are over-coupled; with $C_2 = 3.3\,\text{pF}$, a single peak with low insertion loss (approximately 1 dB) is obtained. This latter case is when the tuned circuits are critically coupled, and this is what should be aimed at for all these filters.

In Table 6.14, two columns are shown for C_2, depending on whether the drive and terminating impedance is $50\,\Omega$ or $75\,\Omega$. The $75\,\Omega$ values tend to be smaller than the $50\,\Omega$ values, but in some cases the values are the same because the lower value tried for the $75\,\Omega$ system resulted in unacceptable insertion loss for the filter and so the $50\,\Omega$ value was used. The use of rather small values for C_2 means that some care has to be taken when building these filters to avoid problems with stray capacitance. Keep the coils close together, and use short leads for C_2. A PCB layout will give the best results.

The practical responses obtained for the $50\,\Omega$ versions of these filters are plotted in Fig. 6.30. To prevent this diagram from becoming too cluttered, only the responses for the six pre-WARC amateur bands are shown; the responses for the other three bands are very similar. The upper limit of the plotted responses is 40 MHz, and the responses for the 7, 14, 21 and 28 MHz filters can be extrapolated above this frequency. All the responses have been plotted with their minimum attenuation level shown as 0 dB. In fact, the filters exhibit some attenuation at all frequencies, of typically 1–2 dB.

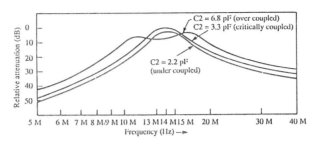

Figure 6.29 *Frequency response of 14 MHz tuned circuit narrow-band filter showing the effect of different values of coupling capacitor, C_2*

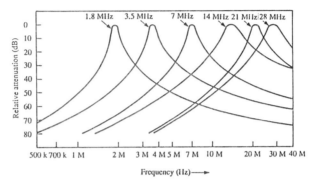

Figure 6.30 *Frequency response of the 1.8, 3.5, 7, 14, 21 and 28 MHz 2 tuned circuit narrow-band filters*

Improving the performance of the narrow-band filters

Although the performance of these two tuned-circuit filters may be adequate for many applications, improved roll-off may be desirable. One method of obtaining this improvement is by cascading filters: the low-impedance output of the first filter is connected to the low-impedance input of the second filter. A considerable improvement in the roll-off will result. However, the improved response is not smooth, having a peak at the high-frequency side of resonance. This is characteristic of all the responses obtained when testing these cascaded configurations and is caused by leakage inductance, which is always seen in practical transformers, especially ones with high turns ratios.

This cascaded arrangement has the advantage of easy alignment. If, when the PCB on which the filter will be built is designed, a link is incorporated in the low-impedance connection between the sections, each section can be aligned separately with the link omitted. The link can then be soldered into place with the confidence that the total network will be correctly aligned.

The filters described provide a comprehensive range of performances for the nine amateur bands below 30 MHz. These designs can be adapted for other frequencies below 30 MHz by choosing a filter closest to the range to be covered and adjusting the values of C_1 and C_3 for resonance close to the desired frequency. The transformer cores can then be adjusted for the exact centre frequency required.

Receiver front-end design

Receiver front-end design is a broad subject and clearly cannot be covered in any detail here. However, it is worthwhile mentioning a few points, with particular reference to fitting the front-end filters into the overall design, to ensure that they are driven and terminated correctly and can achieve their potential performances.

Figure 6.31 shows a typical amateur-band receiver front end. It is intended for use with 50 Ω antennas and so the impedance throughout the system is 50 Ω. Attenuation levels of 0, 10, 20 and 30 dB are selectable by S_1. The ground connection for the attenuator resistors is picked up from the braid of the RF co-ax. used to carry the signal to and from the attenuator switch. Three narrow-band filters are provided, for three-band operation, and mechanical switching of the filters by S_2 is shown. Another gang on S_2 can be used to switch the VFO tuned circuit or frequency-converter crystals to provide the correct local-oscillator input to the first mixer stage. An RF amplifier is shown, which can be switched in or out of circuit by S_3, depending on the band in use and the listening conditions, but it may not be needed at all if all the bands to be covered are below 14 MHz. It can be convenient to build the RF amplifier on its own PCB, separate from the other circuits, so that new designs can easily be tried without disturbing any other modules. The first mixer is driven either by the filter outputs (in which case it must provide the correct termination impedance for the filters) or by the RF amplifier output.

Figure 6.32 shows the front end of a typical general-coverage receiver. Two antenna impedances, 50 Ω and 450 Ω, are catered for. The matching for the 50 Ω antenna is provided by a broad-band transformer. The high-impedance antenna can be connected to the top end of the transformer without any noticeable degradation in performance, avoiding the need to switch antennas. From the top end of the transformer, the system impedance is 450 Ω, allowing the use of broad-band filters using off-the-shelf inductors. As in the amateur-band front end, four levels of attenuation are provided,

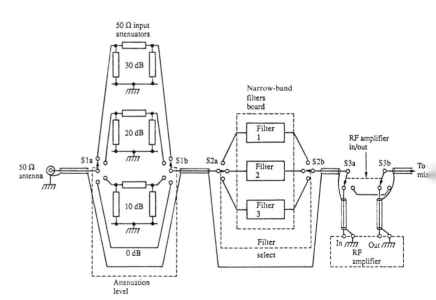

Figure 6.31 *Block diagram of a typical amateur bands front end*

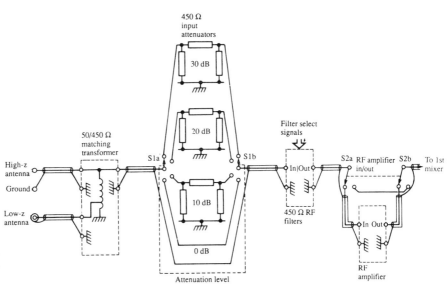

Figure 6.32 *Block diagram of a typical general coverage receiver front end*

and again the first mixer is either driven directly by the filters or by a switchable RF amplifier.

RF filter construction

The layout of an RF filter on a PCB is mainly a matter of common sense. Keep the arrangement of the components similar to that on the circuit diagram: that is, long and thin with the output well away from the input. Etch away as little of the board surface as necessary, using the remaining copper as a ground plane. This keeps all connections to ground very short, ensuring that very little stray inductance exists in any ground path. The ground plane also serves as a screen between adjacent signal paths. For most applications below VHF, it is not necessary to go as far as using double-sided PCB material. For narrow-band filters using Toko 10K transformers, solder the screening can to the ground plane.

To obtain the best performance from the broad-band filters using the 7BS inductors, small earthed vertical screens, made of PCB material, should be soldered between adjacent inductors if space permits. Because these inductors consist of wire wound on small open-sided bobbins, they tend to radiate energy and are susceptible to external fields. This results in a degree of coupling between nearby inductors and can reduce the stop-band attenuation attainable. The author has measured differences of approximately 5 dB in the stop-band attenuation between screened and unscreened layouts. An alternative is to spread the inductors out as much as possible.

Plate 6.2 shows a set of six wide-band filters constructed for a general coverage receiver. The design incorporates electronic switching similar to that shown in Fig. 6.23. The appropriate filter is selected by + 12 volt signals from CMOS logic which decodes the MHz settings of the receiver tuning controls. Plate 6.3 shows a set of nine amateur-band filters using the two-tuned-circuit method. This layout allows pairs of identical filters to be cascaded if required, while still keeping the inputs and outputs separate.

Active filters

A simple approach to using real components has been applied successfully to passive filters, so can the same success be achieved with active filters? If anything, we might expect more success since, with active filters, we do not have to contend with the finite-Q limitations of inductors, which are the

Plate 6.2

Plate 6.3

dominant effect in the degradation of passive filter performance. It is reasonable to assume that the resistors and capacitors used in active filters behave like ideal components at the comparatively low frequencies at which active filters are used. The only effect requiring investigation is what the rounding of component values has on the filter responses.

Figure 6.33 (a) shows the fifth-order Butterworth low-pass filter, first shown in Fig. 4.15 (b), with exact component values. Figure 6.33 (b) shows the filter with rounded component values. Because the response-determining resistors are already $10 \, \text{k}\Omega$, they do not have to be altered. Resistor R_2, the feedback resistor around the first op-amp, has been reduced to $82 \, \text{k}\Omega$, resulting in a reduction in gain for this stage, and the other two feedback resistors, R_6 and R_9, which are in circuit to reduce offset errors, have been rounded to $18 \, \text{k}\Omega$.

Figure 6.34 shows the responses obtained for these two circuits. Curve (a) is the exact-components response and curve (b) is the rounded-components response. As expected, a slight reduction in the passband gain, from 20 dB to

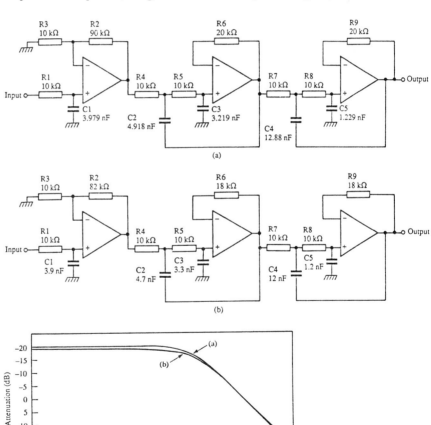

Figure 6.33 *The 5th order Butterworth low-pass filter scaled to 4 kHz cut-off frequency:*
a) With exact component values
b) With rounded component values

Figure 6.34 *Simulated amplitude response of the 5th order Butterworth low-pass filter:*
a) With exact component values
b) With rounded component values

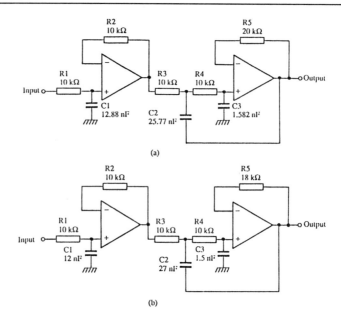

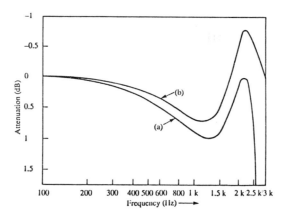

Figure 6.35 *The 3rd order 1 dB passband ripple Chebyshev low-pass filter scaled to 2.5 kHz cut-off frequency:*
a) With exact component values
b) With rounded component values

about 19 dB, has resulted, and the 3dB-down frequency is now 4 kHz, compared with the original value of 3.5 kHz.

If the same approach is applied to the 1 dB passband ripple Chebyshev low-pass filter, originally shown in Fig. 4.17, the circuits of Fig. 6.35 are obtained. Fig. 6.36 shows the simulated responses of the two circuits. The exact-values version of the circuit has a DC gain of 0 dB, which is matched by the rounded-values version response (curve (b)), but a peak in the gain of approximately 0.8 dB is produced just before ripple cut-off. Referring to Fig. 6.35, this should have been anticipated: increasing the value of C_2 to 27 nF (and hence decreasing the reactance of this capacitor) results in more of the output signal being fed back to the non-inverting input of the op-amp, giving a greater peak gain for the second-order section. The stopband response of the two versions of the filter are very similar and the overall performance of the rounded-values filter should be entirely satisfactory.

Figure 6.36 *Amplitude response of the 3rd order 1 dB Chebyshev low-pass filter*
a) With exact component values
b) With rounded component values

Bessel active filters

We have seen that the amplitude responses of Butterworth and Chebyshev filters can still be acceptable when the component values are rounded. Bessel filters, however, are usually chosen for their linear phase responses, and so it is interesting to investigate the effect that rounding has on this aspect of a filter performance.

Figure 6.37 (a) shows the fourth-order Bessel low-pass filter, first shown in Fig. 4.19 (b), and Fig. 6.37 (b) is the rounded-values version. Fig. 6.38 shows the simulated phase responses for these two filters. The linearity of the exact values filter can be seen and the deviation from this ideal produced by rounding the components is less than 2 degrees up to 500 Hz, and again should be entirely satisfactory in practice.

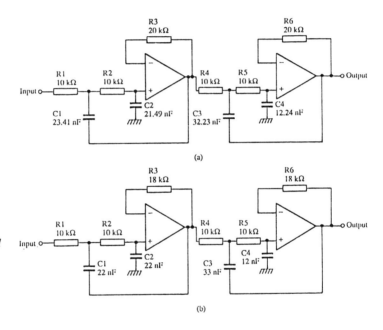

Figure 6.37 *The 4th order Bessel low-pass filter scaled to 500 Hz cut-off frequency:*
a) With exact component values
b) With rounded component values

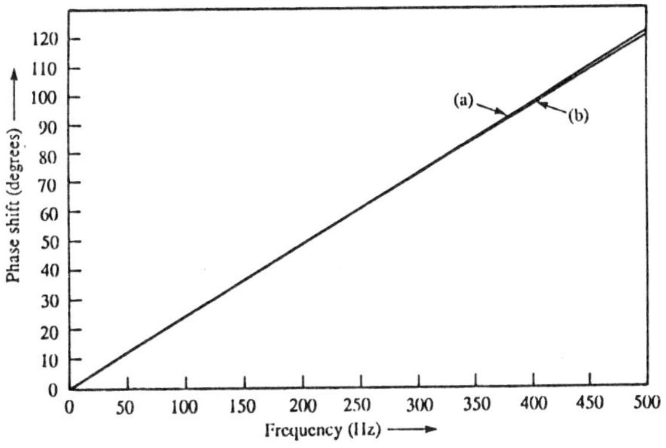

Figure 6.38 *Simulated phase response of the 4th order Bessel low-pass filter:*
a) With exact component values
b) With rounded component values

Active band-pass filters

Figure 6.39 (a) shows the MFBP filter, originally shown in Fig. 5.15, and Fig. 6.39 (b) is the circuit with rounded-component values. The exact and rounded values for R_1 and R_2, for band-pass Q of 2, 5, 10 and 20 are shown in Table 6.15. Fig. 6.40 shows the simulated responses for the four sets of rounded-component values. Two effects are evident: firstly, the resonant frequency of the section varies from the 1 kHz nominal and secondly, the peak gains are slightly different from the exact component responses. For example, for the band-pass $Q=2$ case, the peak gain of the exact-components filter was 18.06 dB (at 1 kHz), compared with 18.95 dB at 1150 Hz for the rounded-components version. All the rounded versions show some deviation from the exact-component filters, all the variations in resonant frequency being to a slightly higher frequency, the peak gains showing worst case variations of about +1 dB.

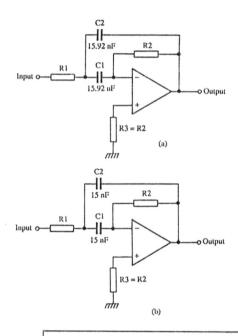

Figure 6.39 *The MFBP filter scaled to 1 kHz:*
a) With exact component values
b) With rounded component values
Values for R_1, R_2 and R_3 are shown in Tale 6.15

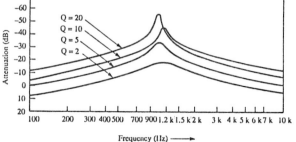

Figure 6.40 *Simulated amplitude response of the MFBP section with rounded component values. Responses for nominal band-pass Q values of 2, 5, 10 and 20 are shown.*

Table 6.15 *Exact and rounded resistor values for the MFBP filter*

BANDPASS Q	EXACT VALUES		ROUNDED VALUES	
	R1(ohm)	R2(ohm)	R1(ohm)	R2(ohm)
2	2500	40k	2.2k	39k
5	1000	100k	1k	100k
10	500	200k	470	180k
20	250	400k	270	390k

Active band-stop filters

The design of narrow-band active band-stop filters, described in Chapter 5, depends on the cancellation of the input signal by summing with a 180 degree phase-shifted version produced by a band-pass filter. Any slight modification in the resonant frequency of the band-pass filter is unlikely to be important, but the method relies on accurate matching between the amplitude of the input signal and that of the phase-shifted signal at the band-pass filter output. Fig. 6.41 shows a band-stop filter, centred nominally on 700 Hz, using rounded component values but with the output of the band-pass filter fed to the summing block via a 22 kΩ trimmer, R_6. This allows the gain for this input to be varied, allowing a setting to be achieved where a deep notch is obtained. Two values for R_1 are shown, allowing for band-stop Q of nominally 3 and 5.

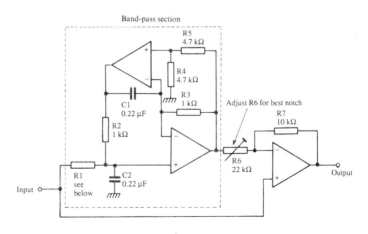

Figure 6.41 *The 700 Hz DABP notch filter with R_6 replaced by a trimmer potentiometer, rounded values for R_1 are shown for band-stop Q values of 3 and 5*

Nominal Q_{bs}	R1
3	3.3 kΩ
5	4.7 kΩ

Single rail operation

All the active filter circuits shown so far have assumed that the op-amps are operated from a split-rail supply: that is, having a positive voltage, a negative voltage and ground midway between the positive and negative rails. This assumption greatly simplifies the presentation of circuit diagrams, as the supply pins on the op-amps do not have to be shown and non-inverting inputs can be shown connected to ground, either directly or via a resistor. This arrangement is not convenient, however, when circuits are built, especially if they are being incorporated into existing equipment having only a single positive rail. Fortunately, it is simple to adapt the circuits to work from such single-rail supplies.

Some op-amps are advertisd as 'single-rail' devices. This does not mean that they can be used from single-rail supplies in dual-rail configurations, and they require the same treatment as 'ordinary' op-amps. What the phrase is intended to mean is that they can operate from lower supply voltages and so single-rail operation is generally easier to achieve.

In the single-rail configuration, an op-amp must still have three voltages aplied to it: the third voltage, besides the positive supply and ground, is a mid-rail reference used to bias the inputs. Fig. 6.42 shows two mid-rail voltage generators. Fig. 6.42 (a) is a simple resistor potential divider chain consisting of two equal resistors, with the mid-rail decoupled by a capacitor. Fig. 6.42 (b) has an op-amp voltage follower added whose output is at a much lower impedance than the simple potential divider circuit. Circuit (a) can be used where mid-rail voltages are generated locally for each op-amp needing the reference, whereas with circuit (b) the reference can be distributed across several op-amps.

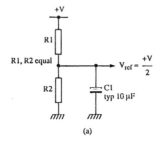

(a)

Figure 6.42 *Generation of a mid-rail reference voltage:*
a) Using a potential divider network
b) Using a potential divider network buffered by an op-amp voltage follower stage.

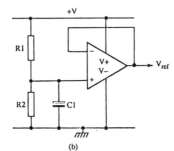

(b)

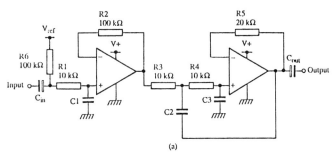

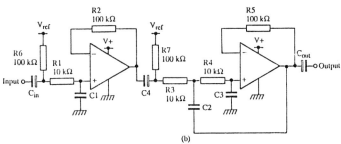

Figure 6.43 *Two methods of operating a 3rd order active filter from a single supply rail:*
a) Has one V_{ref} feed, with the second op-amp obtaining its bias from the first stage
b) has the two stages DC isolated from each other, each stage having its own V_{ref} feed

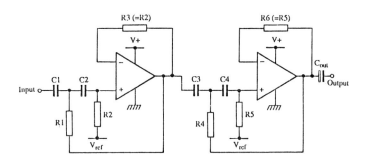

Figure 6.44 *A 4th order active high-pass filter biased for single rail operation*

Figure 6.43 (a) shows a third-order active filter configured for single rail operation. In the upper diagram, a single source of the mid-rail reference is fed into the first op-amp non-inverting input circuit, providing the bias for this input. Rather than feed this voltage directly to the op-amp input, it is coupled to the junction of the input capacitor and R_1. At this point, the resistance to V_{ref} does not have an effect on the frequency response of the stage, since the node is driven by the, presumably, low-impedance output of the preceding stage. The non-inverting input of the second stage of the filter derives its bias voltage from the ouput of the first stage; DC isolation of the entire filter is provided by C_{in} and C_{out}.

Figure 6.43 (b) shows how the DC conditions of two sections of the filter can be made independent of each other. Capacitor C_4 performs the DC blocking function, and R_6 and R_7 provide mid-rail feeds to each op-amp. Strictly speaking, the filter response is no longer low-pass in nature, since C_4 adds a high-pass characteristic. However, the comparatively high impedance level of the second stage means that if a reasonable value is used for C_4 (say

10μ F) the cut-off frequency of the high-pass response is so low as to be unnoticeable. It is immaterial whether the earthy ends of C_1 and C_3 are connected to ground or to V_{ref}, since V_{ref} should itself be decoupled to ground.

A high-pass active filter can be adapted to single-rail operation very easily, as shown in Fig. 6.44 for a fourth-order filter. The response-determining capacitors provide DC isolation at the input and between stages, and the resistors from the non-inverting inputs are convenient V_{ref} feed paths.

Summary and conclusions

When any electronic circuit is built and tested, the performance obtained differs from that originally predicted   because of the effects of using real components. Filters are no exception to this general rule, but are often mistakenly viewed as being more sensitive to component variations than other circuits.

With passive audio filters, it was shown that rounding the component values to the nearest E12 preferred value had little effect on the performance. A more noticeable cause of degradation of performance was the finite Q of the inductors used to build these filters, and the characteristics of the degradation can be summarized as non-zero insertion loss at all frequencies; an increase in the magnitude of passband ripple; rounding of the response close to cut-off; shifts in the cut-off, start of stopband and high attenuation frequencies; and finite rather than infinite, attenuations in the stopband for elliptic filters.

When these degradations are compared with the effects other elements produce in an audio path, the contributions made by the filter are not significant. If required, some smoothing of the passband response of a passive low-pass filter can be obtained by the judicious selection of the value of a capacitor in the drive circuit, forming a band-pass filter. By using the Toko 10RB and 10RBH range of inductors, high performance and very compact passive audio filters can be built, which have advantages over active filters in not requiring power supplies and not contributing noise to the system.

Several methods of driving and terminating a passive audio filter were described which ensured that the correct impedances are presented to the filter input and output. Bipolar transistors, FETs, op-amps and transformers are all suitable components for interfacing to audio filters.

RF passive filters suffer less from the effects of real components than their audio counterparts, even if preferred-value, ready-wound inductors, such as those in the Toko 7BS range, are used for their construction. This is because the Q of these components is higher than the inductors used in audio filters. The constructor has to be careful with the initial choice of cut-off frequency of a filter design intended for rounding so that the shift due to the rounding process does not cause a greater than desired attenuation at the band edges.

A range of wide-band RF band-pass filters suitable for use in the front end of a general coverage receiver was presented. The design method adopted was to cascade low-pass and high-pass sections, and the filters used entirely standard, preferred value components. By careful choice of the input and output impedance of these filters, inductance values were obtained which enabled Toko inductors to be used. The impedance settled on for the designs presented was $450\,\Omega$, which, as well as giving the benefit of easy implementation, also allows simple broad-band transformers to be designed to allow the use of $50\,\Omega$ and $75\,\Omega$ antennas.

Two methods of switching these wide-band filters were shown, including mechanical switches and an electronic scheme using diodes. It was seen that the choice of the minimum-inductor or minimum-capacitor configuration for the high-pass section in the band-pass filter effects the ease of implementation of the electronic switching method. The design of a broad-band transformer which enables $50\,\Omega$ and $75\,\Omega$ antennas to be used was described. This is simple to construct and has been found to give better practical results than many toroid-based designs tried.

The usefulness of constant-impedance attenuators was pointed out and designs for $50\,\Omega$, $75\,\Omega$ and $450\,\Omega$ networks with attenuation values up to $40\,dB$ tabulated. Data was presented to enable networks for any impedance and attenuation level to be produced.

A range of narrow-band filters for the amateur bands, constructed with ready wound Toko transformers, was described. Because the amateur bands have rather high band-pass Q requirements, a compromise has to be accepted between the ease of construction of suitable filters and a mismatch between the ideal band-pass Q requirement of the band to be covered and what can be achieved in practice. The performance of these filters can be improved by cascading, connecting the low-impedance output of one section to the low-impedance input of another.

A brief outline of how wide-band and narrow-band filters can be incorporated into receiver front ends while maintaining correct input and output impedance matches was given. Outline front-end designs were shown, one suitable for a general coverage receiver, and the other suitable for an amateur-bands receiver.

To achieve the predicted performance from RF filters in practice, it is necessary to use sensible constructional techniques. In particular, the use of a ground plane guarantees short connections to ground and the plane also has a shielding effect between signal paths. Laying the components of a filter out in a straight line on a PCB, keeping the output well away from the input is good practice, reducing signal leakage around the filter to a minimum.

The rounding of component values was successfully applied to Butterworth and Chebyshev active filters. Because inductors are not used in active filters, the degradation caused to passive filter responses by low-Q components is not seen with active filters. The Chebyshev filter investigated showed that the peak gain of such a filter close to cut-off can become excessive because of unforeseen rounding effects. Therefore, care should be taken with all second order sections that the gain does not peak excessively. When the component values of a Bessel low-pass filter were rounded and the new phase response was obtained, only a very small deviation from the ideal was seen.

Narrow-band, active, band-pass filters suffer slight shifts in the resonant frequency and variation in the peak gain when the rounding process is applied. Although this is unimportant in most band-pass applications, when a band-pass filter is used as the phase shifting element in a narrow-band band-stop filter, it is best to incorporate a gain trimming potentiometer so that accurate cancellation can be obtained.

Many applications of active filters require single-rail operation of the op-amps. This is simple to achieve by the generation of a mid-supply voltage and the use of this voltage to bias the op-amp inputs. Active low-pass filters consisting of several sections can be treated in one of two ways: they can either have only the first section inputs biased by the reference voltage, successive sections then deriving their bias from the preceding section; or the sections can be DC-isolated from each other using capacitors and separate references applied to each section. The latter solution has the advantage that DC offsets do not accumulate through the filter, but the circuit will no longer act as a true low-pass filter, because DC and low-frequency signals will be attenuated by the high-pass action of the capacitors.

In conclusion, it has been demonstrated, using computer simulations and practical results, that filters of all types can successfully be built using preferred-value components and ready-wound inductors, so long as some compromises in the performance can be tolerated. In the amateur field, these compromises are generally acceptable, especially when the ease of construction of such filters is taken into account. Many practical designs have been presented, but these represent only a small proportion of the many potential users of filters in all aspects of electronics.

References

1. E. Wetherhold, *Elliptic Lowpass Audio Filter Design*, February 1984, Ham Radio, p. 20, W3NQN.
2. E. Wetherhold, *Simplified Lowpass Filter Construction Using Surplus 88 mH Inductors*, April 1983, Radio Communication, W3NQN.
3. P.R. Geffe, *Simplified Modern Filter Design*, 1963, John F. Rider, p. 58.
4. S. Niewiadomski. *Passive Audio Filter Design, part 3: attenuation equalisers*, January 1986, Ham Radio.
5. *Mullard Technical Handbook, Book 3, Part 5, AD4090/X series loudspeakers*, August, 1978.
6. D.L. Richards, *Telecommunications by Speech*, 1973, Butterworths, p. 83.
7. ARRL, *ARRL 1985 Handbook*, Chapter 11, p. 15–16.
8. ARRL, *Solid State Design for the Radio Amateur*, 1977, p. 55–6.
9. C. Bowick, *RF Circuit Design*, 1985, Sams, p. 161–3.
10. F. Ogden and T. Bailey, *Meet the Micron!*, May–July 1985, Ham Radio Today.

7 Filter design software

The cheapness and easy availability of modern computers have affected many aspects of electronics. To take amateur radio as an example, programs are now available for Morse code and RTTY coding and decoding, propagation path prediction, satellite orbit calculations, log keeping, and many other applications. Although such programs are undoutedly useful, there seems to be a lack of good software to help with circuit design, and particularly with the design of filters.

Many of the steps in the filter design process lend themselves to a degree of automation using computer programs. Routine processes such as scaling normalized components to their final frequency and impedance levels simply remove some of the tedium of filter design, especially if the steps have to be repeated many times until reasonable component values are obtained. On the other hand, computer programs allow the design of completely new filters, specifically tailored to particular applications, rather than having to rely on the catalogues presented in Chapters 2 and 4.

It would be possible to write a single, highly complex, program to handle the whole of the filter design process covered in this book. The program could be menu-driven, taking the user through all the choices available at each step, and turning a specification into a final practical filter design. The drawback with this approach is that not all users will want such a comprehensive program and may require only a small part of the total program. The onus is therefore placed on those who want a comprehensive package to merge together the individual programs presented here.

The programs presented in this chapter are written in BASIC for the Sinclair Spectrum computer, although the author recognises that many other types of computer are in use. To aid the conversion of programs to other languages or computers, statements are avoided which might cause problems. Similarly, the graphical display of results, which again can make conversion difficult, is avoided. Details of the specific dialect of BASIC implemented on a particular machine will be found in the language manual accompanying it. Guidance is given in reference 1 on the conversion of programs to run on other machines.

No claims are made for elegance of design for the programs: the main criteria has been to obtain programs that work, rather than worrying about the niceties of structure. Also, little effort has been made to make them 'idiot proof': if, for example, negative normalized component values are input to the component scaling programs, then negative scaled values will be obtained.

In previous chapters, much emphasis has been placed on the usefulness of circuit simulation for verifying filter performance before circuits are built. Writing a simulation package is not a trivial task and so a review of a reasonably priced, commercially available circuit simulator which is available for several computers has been included in this chapter, along with details of other simulators known to the author. This approach overcomes two problems: firstly, considerable effort would have been required to write a new simulator, and secondly, the limited space available in this book would have made it impossible to give a listing of the program.

Butterworth/Chebyshev order estimation (program 7.1)

Estimating the order required for a Butterworth filter to satisfy a stopband filtering requirement can be carried out using Fig. 2.9 as a nomograph. If an accurate estimate is required, or if the order works out to be greater than 7, a general equation is useful. Equation 2.5, reproduced below as equation 7.1, is such an equation.

$$n = \frac{\log_{10}[10^{A/10} - 1]}{2 \log_{10}\left(\dfrac{\omega}{\omega_c}\right)} \tag{7.1}$$

where A is the stop-band attenuation in dB,
 ω_c is the cut-off frequency,
 ω is the frequency at which the attenuation is specified.

Estimating the order of a Chebyshev filter is more complex because a new variable, the passband ripple, has been introduced. Equation 2.11 gives the stopband attenuation at any frequency for a Chebyshev filter and can be re-arranged to give the order n of a filter to meet a specification, as shown below

$$n = \frac{\cosh^{-1}\sqrt{\dfrac{10^{A/10} - 1}{\varepsilon^2}}}{\cosh^{-1}\left(\dfrac{\omega}{\omega_c}\right)} \tag{7.2}$$

where A is the stopband attenuation in dB,
 ω_c is the cut-off frequency,
 ω is the frequency at which the attenuation is specified,
 ε is the ripple factor.

Since inverse hyperbolic functions (such as $\cosh^{-1}x$) are not available on many computers, a useful relationship is:

$$\cosh^{-1}x = \ln\left(x + \sqrt{x^2 - 1}\right) \tag{7.3}$$

```
5          REM This program is called ORDER (Spectrum version)

100        INPUT "Butterworth or Chebyshev (b/c):";f$
110        IF f$ = "b" THEN GO TO 200
120        IF f$ = "c" THEN GO TO 300
130        REM invalid input
140        PRINT "invalid filter type, try again"
150        GO TO 100

200        REM Butterworth filter
210        INPUT "Type cut-off frequency:";fcut
220        INPUT "required attenuation (dB):";atten
230        INPUT "at a frequency of:";fatten
240        LET n = LN(10↑(atten/10)-1)/(2*LN(fatten/fcut))
250        GO TO 1000

300        REM Chebyshev filter
310        INPUT "Type ripple cut-off frequency:";fcut
320        INPUT "required attenuation (dB):";atten
330        INPUT "at a frequency of:";fatten
340        INPUT "passband ripple (dB):";ripple
350        LET etaeta = 10↑(ripple/10)-1
360        LET x = SQR((10↑(atten/10)-1)/etaeta)
370        LET y = fatten/fcut
380        LET n = LN(x+SQR((x*x)-1))/LN(y+SQR((y*y)-1))
390        GO TO 1000

1000       REM order rounding and print routine
1010       LET nround = INT(n)+1
1020       PRINT "exact order = ";n
1030       PRINT "rounded order = ";nround
1040       STOP
```

Program 7.1 (ORDER)

Program 7.1 (ORDER) implements these equations. If the answer 'b' is given after the prompt for the filter type, the program works out the order of a Butterworth filter after further prompting for the appropriate values. The cut-off frequency and the frequency at which the stop-band attenuation is specified can be in rad/s or Hz, so long as they are both in the same units. The Butterworth section of the program takes advantage of the fact that the value of the ratio of the logarithms of two numbers is independent of the base of the logarithms. Therefore, although the logarithms are taken to base 10 in equation 7.1, the Spectrum program uses logarithms to base e, which are all that are available in Spectrum BASIC.

If the answer 'c' is given after the prompt for the filter type, the program works out the order of a Chebyshev filter from equation 7.2. One additional value for the filter specification, the passband ripple, is required in the

Chebyshev case. As for the Butterworth filter, the cut-off frequency and the frequency at which the stopband attenuation is specified can be in rad/s or Hz.

As well as printing the exact value of filter order needed to satisfy a specification, the program also rounds the order upwards and prints this value out. The orders estimated are equally valid for passive and active implementations of the filters.

Passive low-pass Butterworth filter design (program 7.2)

Table 2.1 in Chapter 2 gives normalized component values for equal source and termination impedance, passive Butterworth filters of orders from 2 to 7. Calculation of component values for Butterworth filters with equal source and termination impedances is fairly simple and equation 2.6 was presented to enable this to be performed if orders greater than 7 are required. If filters with unequal source and termination impedances are required, the calculations are not so simple and this section describes the designs of such filters[2] and gives a program to perform the calculations.

Figure 7.1 shows two implementations of passive Butterworth low-pass filters: circuit (a) has a shunt capacitor C_1 closest to the output, whereas circuit (b) has a series inductor L_1 closest to the output. Both circuits have source impedances of 1 Ω. With filters having equal source and termination impedances, the circuits are duals of each other and either implementation can be used. When a filter with unequal source and termination impedances is required, only one implementation is suitable: circuit (a) can be used where the termination impedance is greater than or equal to the source impedance, and circuit (b) can be used where the termination impedance is less than or equal to the source impedance.

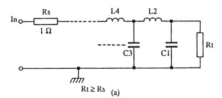

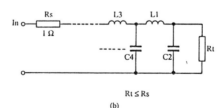

Figure 7.1 *Passive low-pass Butterworth filter implementations*

The first step in the calculation of the component values is to determine the factor λ, which is given by

$$\lambda = \left(\frac{R_t - 1}{R_t + 1} \right)^{1/n} \text{ for } R_t \geqslant R_s \tag{7.4}$$

or:

$$\lambda = \left(\frac{1 - R_t}{1 + R_t} \right)^{1/n} \text{ for } R_t \leqslant R_s \tag{7.5}$$

where R_t is the termination impedance,
      R_s is the source impedance $(1\ \Omega)$,
      n is the order of the filter.

```
5        REM This program is called PASSBUT (Spectrum version)

100      INPUT "Type filter order:";n
110      INPUT "termination impedance (ohm):";rl

200      IF rl>1 THEN LET lambda =  ((rl-1)/(rl+1))↑(1/n)
210      IF rl<1 THEN LET lambda =  ((1-rl)/(rl+1))↑(1/n)
220      IF rl=1 THEN LET lambda =  0

300      PRINT "Component designations are from output to input"
310      REM first component value
320      LET a = 2*SIN(PI/(2*n))
330      IF rl>1 THEN GO TO 400
340      GO TO 500

400      LET comp = a/(rl*(1-lambda))
410      PRINT "C1=";comp;" F"
420      GO TO 600

500      LET comp = (a*rl)/(1-lambda)
510      IF rl<1 THEN PRINT "L1=";comp;" H"
520      IF rl=1 THEN PRINT "C1/L1=";comp;" F/H"

600      REM calculating other components
610      FOR m=1 TO n/2
620      LET comp = (4*SIN((PI*(4*m-3))/(2*n))*SIN((PI*(4*m-1))/(2*n)))/
         ((1-lambda*2*COS(PI*(4*m-2)/(2*n))+lambda↑2)*comp)
630      IF rl>1 THEN PRINT "L";2*m;"=";comp;" H"
640      IF rl=1 THEN PRINT "L";2*m;"/C";2*m;"=";comp;" H/F"
650      IF rl<1 THEN PRINT "C";2*m;"=";comp;" F"

700      IF n<=2*m THEN STOP
710      LET comp = (4*SIN((PI*(4*m-1))/(2*n))*SIN((PI*(4*m+1))/(2*n)))/
         ((1-lambda*2*COS(PI*4*m/(2*n))+lambda↑2)*comp)
720      IF rl>1 THEN PRINT "C";2*m+1;"=";comp;" F"
730      IF rl=1 THEN PRINT "C";2*m+1;"/L";2*m+1;"=";comp;" F/H"
740      IF rl<1 THEN PRINT "L";2*m+1;"=";comp;" H"

800      NEXT m
```

Program 7.2 (PASSBUT)

The value of the first component can now be calculated from the expressions

$$C_1 = \frac{\alpha_1}{R_t(1-\lambda)} \quad \text{for } R_t \geqslant R_s \tag{7.6}$$

or

$$L_1 = \frac{\alpha_1 R_t}{(1-\lambda)} \quad \text{for } R_t \leqslant R_s \tag{7.7}$$

where α_1 is obtained by substituting $i = 1$ into the expression

$$\alpha_i = 2 \sin \frac{\pi i}{2n} \tag{7.8}$$

The remaining component values are now calculated by stepping m from 1 to $(n-1)/2$ for n odd, or to $n/2$ for n even, in the following equations

$$C_{2m-1} L_{2m} = \frac{\alpha_{4m-3}\,\alpha_{4m-1}}{1 - \lambda\beta_{4m-2} + \lambda^2} \tag{7.9}$$

and

$$C_{2m+1} L_{2m} = \frac{\alpha_{4m-1}\,\alpha_{4m+1}}{1 - \lambda\beta_{4m} + \lambda^2} \tag{7.10}$$

for $R_t \geqslant R_s$,

or

$$L_{2m-1}\,C_{2m} = \frac{\alpha_{4m-3}\,\alpha_{4m-1}}{1 - \lambda\beta_{4m-2} + \lambda^2} \tag{7.11}$$

and

$$L_{2m+1}\,C_{2m} = \frac{\lambda_{4m-1}\,\lambda_{4m+1}}{1 - \lambda\beta_{4m} + \lambda^2} \tag{7.12}$$

for $R_t \geqslant R_s$,

where α_i is given by Equation 7.8 and β_i is given by

$$\beta_i = 2 \cos \frac{\pi i}{2n} \tag{7.13}$$

Program 7.2 (PASSBUT) implements these equations. A major portion of the program is concerned with determining whether a particular component is a capacitor or an inductor and printing out the normalized component value preceded by a component designation. Note that, in Fig. 7.1, the component designations are in sequence from the output towards the input. The designations produced by PASSBUT correspond to Fig. 7.1: that is, the value of the component closest to the output is printed first, and is either shunt capacitor C_1 or series inductor L_1. If an equal source and termination impedance filter is specified, the print out indicates that each component value refers to either a shunt capacitor or a series inductor.

Passive low-pass Chebyshev filter design (program 7.3)

In Chapter 2, Tables 2.2–2.8 give normalized component values for passive Chebyshev filters of orders from 2 to 7 with two values of source and termination impedance and seven magnitudes of passband ripple. Filters with orders greater than 7, with other values of source and termination impedances, or with different passband ripple magnitudes than those shown in the tables may be required, and this section describes the design of such filters.[3] The technique is similar to Butterworth filter design described previously, but is more complex because of the incorporation of an extra variable, the passband ripple.

The first step is to calculate the quantity a, from the termination impedance and the ripple factor, using the expression

$$a = \frac{4R_t}{(R_t + 1)^2} \quad \text{when } n \text{ is odd} \tag{7.14}$$

or

$$a = \frac{4R_t}{(R_t + 1)^2}[1 + \varepsilon^2] \quad \text{when } n \text{ is even} \tag{7.15}$$

Where R_t is the termination impedance,
ε is the ripple factor,
n is the order of the filter

In the case where the filter order is even, a test must be carried out on the value of a, and the specification can only be implemented if a is less than or equal to 1.
Then by letting

$$\alpha_i = 2 \sin \frac{\pi i}{2n} \tag{7.16}$$

$$\beta_i = 2 \cos \frac{\pi i}{2n} \tag{7.17}$$

$$\gamma = \left[\frac{1}{\varepsilon} + \sqrt{\frac{1}{\varepsilon^2} + 1}\right]^{1/n} \tag{7.18}$$

$$\delta = \left[\sqrt{\frac{1-a}{\varepsilon^2}} + \sqrt{\frac{1-a}{\varepsilon^2} + 1}\right]^{1/n} \tag{7.19}$$

$$x = \gamma - \frac{1}{\gamma} \tag{7.20}$$

and

$$y = \delta - \frac{1}{\delta} \tag{7.21}$$

```
5        REM This program is called PASSCHEB (Spectrum version)

100      INPUT "Type filter order:";n
110      INPUT "passband ripple (dB):";ap
120      INPUT "termination impedance (ohm):";rl

200      LET refl = SQR(10↑(ap/10)-1)
210      REM test for n odd
220      IF n = 2*(INT(n/2)+0.5) THEN GO TO 400

300      REM n must be even
310      LET o$ = "even"
320      LET a = (1+refl↑2)*4*rl/((rl+1)↑2)
330      IF a<=1 THEN GO TO 500
340      REM a> 1, therefore can't implement this specification
350      PRINT "Can't implement this specification"
360      STOP

400      REM n is odd
410      LET o$ = "odd"
420      LET a = 4*rl/((rl+1)↑2)

500      LET x = (1/refl+SQR((1/refl↑2)+1))↑(1/n)
510      LET y = (SQR((1-a)/refl↑2)+SQR(((1-a)/refl↑2)+1))↑(1/n)
520      LET x1 = x-1/x
530      LET y1 = y-1/y
540      LET num1 = PI/(2*n)

600      REM first component value
610      LET comp = (4*SIN(num1))/(x1-y1)

700      IF o$="odd" AND rl>1 THEN PRINT "L1 = ";comp;"H"
710      IF o$="odd" AND rl=1 THEN PRINT "C1/L1 = ";comp;"F/H"
720      IF o$="odd" AND rl<1 THEN PRINT "C1 = ";comp;"F"
730      IF o$="even" AND rl<1 THEN PRINT "C1 = ";comp;"F"
740      IF o$="even" AND rl>1 THEN PRINT "L1 = ";comp;"H"

800      FOR m=1 TO n/2
810      LET b = x1↑2-2*x1*y1*COS((4*m-2)*num1)+y1↑2 +(2*SIN((4*m-2)*num1))↑2
820      LET comp = (16*SIN((4*m-3)*num1)*SIN((4*m-1)*num1))/(b*comp)
830      IF o$="odd" AND rl>1 THEN PRINT "C";2*m;"= ";comp;"F"
840      IF o$="odd" AND rl=1 THEN PRINT "L";2*m;"/C";2*m;"= ";comp;"H/F"
850      IF o$="odd" AND rl<1 THEN PRINT "L";2*m;"= ";comp;"H"
860      IF o$="even" AND rl<1 THEN PRINT "L";2*m;"= ";comp;"H"
870      IF o$="even" AND rl>1 THEN PRINT "C";2*m;"= ";comp;"F"

900      IF n<=2*m THEN STOP
910      LET b = x1↑2 - 2*x1*y1*COS(4*m*num1) + y1↑2 + (2*SIN(4*m*num1))↑2
920      LET comp = (16*SIN((4*m-1)*num1)*SIN((4*m+1)*num1))/(b*comp)
930      IF o$="odd" AND rl>1 THEN PRINT "L";2*m+1;"= ";comp;"H"
940      IF o$="odd" AND rl=1 THEN
         PRINT "C";2*m+1;"/L";2*m+1;"= ";comp;"F/H"
950      IF o$="odd" AND rl<1 THEN PRINT "C";2*m+1;"= ";comp;"F"
960      IF o$="even" AND rl<1 THEN PRINT "C";2*m+1;"= ";comp;"F"
970      IF o$="even" AND rl>1 THEN PRINT "L";2*m+1;"= ";comp;"H"

1000     NEXT m
```

Program 7.3 (PASSCHEB)

The value of the first capacitor can be calculated from the expression

$$C_1 = \frac{2\alpha_1}{x - y} \tag{7.22}$$

The remaining component values are now calculated by stepping m from 1 to $(n-1)/2$ for n odd, or to $n/2$ for n even, in the following equations

$$C_{2m-1} \, L_{2m} = \frac{4\alpha_{4m-3} \, \alpha_{4m-1}}{b_{2m-1} \, (x,y)} \tag{7.23}$$

and

$$C_{2m+1} \, L_{2m} = \frac{4\alpha_{4m-1} \, \alpha_{4m+1}}{b_{2m}(x,y)} \tag{7.24}$$

where the function $b_i \, (x,y)$ is defined by:

$$b_i \, (x,y) = x^2 - \beta_{2i}xy + y^2 + \alpha_{2i}^2 \tag{7.25}$$

Program 7.3 (**PASSCHEB**) performs these calculations, after prompting for the appropriate values.

```
5        REM This program is called CSCALE (Spectrum version)

100      INPUT "Type final frequency (Hz):";freq
110      INPUT "and final impedance (ohm):";imped
120      INPUT "normalised capacitor value (F):";ncap
130      LET scap = ncap/(2*PI*freq*imped)
140      REM now get it printed
150      LET prcap = scap
160      GO SUB 1000
170      GO TO 120

1000     REM capacitor adjusting and print subroutine
1010     IF prcap<1e-9 THEN GO TO 1100
1020     IF prcap<1e-7 THEN GO TO 1200
1030     GO TO 1300

1100     REM value will be printed in pF
1110     LET prcap = prcap*1e12
1120     PRINT "scaled capacitor value = ";prcap;"pF"
1130     RETURN

1200     REM value will be printed in nF
1210     LET prcap = prcap*1e9
1220     PRINT "scaled capacitor value = ";prcap;"nF"
1230     RETURN

1300     REM value will be printed in uF
1310     LET prcap = prcap*1e6
1320     PRINT "scaled capacitor value = ";prcap;"uF"
1330     RETURN
```

Program 7.4 (CSCALE)

Component scaling (programs 7.4 and 7.5)

The scaling of filter components from their 1 rad/s, 1 Ω values to their final frequency and impedance is a vital part of the modern filter design process. Equations 2.14 and 2.15, reproduced here as equations 7.26 and 7.27, show how the scaling is carried out

$$C = C_n \frac{1}{2\pi f R} \tag{7.26}$$

$$L = L_n \frac{R}{2\pi f} \tag{7.27}$$

Scaling can be a tedious process, especially if many components have to be scaled and several different scaled impedance and frequency combinations have to be tried. Two programs are shown here, one to scale capacitors (program 7.4, CSCALE) and the other to scale inductors (program 7.5, LSCALE). As well as scaling the components, the programs adjust the scaled value and print it in pF, nF or μF for capacitors, and μH, mH or H for

```
5          REM This program is called LSCALE (Spectrum version)

100        INPUT "Type final frequency (Hz):";freq
110        INPUT "and final impedance (ohm):";imped
120        INPUT "normalised inductor value (H):";nind
130        LET sind = nind*imped/(2*PI*freq)
140        REM now get it printed
150        LET prind = sind
160        GO SUB 2000
170        GO TO 120

2000       REM inductor adjusting and print subroutine
2010       IF prind<1e-3 THEN GO TO 2100
2020       IF prind<1 THEN GO TO 2200
2030       GO TO 2300

2100       REM value will be printed in uH
2110       LET prind = prind*1e6
2120       PRINT "scaled inductor value = ";prind;"uH"
2130       RETURN

2200       REM value will be printed in mH
2210       LET prind = prind*1e3
2220       PRINT "scaled inductor value = ";prind;"mH"
2230       RETURN

2300       REM value will be printed in H
2310       PRINT "scaled inductor value = ";prind;"H"
2320       RETURN
```

Program 7.5 (LSCALE)

inductors. Note that the parts of the programs which adjust and print the values are constructed as subroutines starting at line 1000 (in CSCALE) and line 2000 (in LSCALE). This is so that these subroutines can be used in later programs, simplifying the entry of these routines by use of the MERGE command[4]. The statement following the subroutine return causes the prompt for another normalized component value to be printed. If the final frequency and impedance need to be modified each time the scaling process is carried out, line 170 in the programs can be changed to GO TO 100.

The low-pass to high-pass transformation (program 7.6)

It was shown in Chapter 3 that a transformation can be carried out on the components of a passive low-pass filter to convert it into a high-pass filter. The transformation is simply to transform all capacitors into inductors, inductors into capacitors, and to give the new components values equal to the inverse of the prototype values, as shown in Fig. 3.6.

Program 7.6 (LPHPTRAN) performs this transformation, scaling the high-pass component to its final frequency and impedance, and printing the value in its adjusted form by using the incorporated subroutines from CSCALE and LSCALE.

The low-pass to band-pass transformation (program 7.7)

In Chapter 3, a transformation was shown to enable a band-pass filter to be obtained from a low-pass prototype. Each low-pass capacitor is resonated with a parallel inductor, and each low-pass inductor is resonated with a series capacitor at the geometric centre frequency of the desired band-pass response.

The value of a band-pass inductor is therefore given by

$$L_\mathrm{p} = \frac{1}{4\pi^2 f_0^2 C_\mathrm{L}} \tag{7.28}$$

and the value of a band-pass capacitor is given by

$$C_\mathrm{p} = \frac{1}{4\pi^2 f_0^2 L_\mathrm{L}} \tag{7.29}$$

Program 7.7 (LPBPTRAN) performs the transformation, prompting for the lower and upper band-pass cut-off frequencies, the final impedance, and printing out the scaled band-pass component values, making use of the CSCALE and LSCALE subroutines.

Active low-pass Chebyshev filter design (program 7.8)

In Chapter 4, Tables 4.3–4.9 give values of d and ω_0 for the sections of active low-pass Chebyshev filters of orders from 2 to 10, with seven magnitudes of

```
5          REM This program is called LPHPTRAN (Spectrum version)

100        INPUT "Type final frequency (Hz):";freq
110        INPUT "and final impedance (ohm):";imped
200        INPUT "Capacitor or inductor (c/l):";c$
210        IF c$ = "l" THEN GO TO 300
220        IF c$ = "c" THEN GO TO 600
230        REM invalid input
240        PRINT "invalid component type, try again"
250        GO TO 200

300        REM lowpass component is an inductor
310        INPUT "type normalised lowpass inductor value (H):";nlpind
320        LET shpcap = (1/nlpind)/(2*PI*freq*imped)
330        REM now get it printed
340        LET prcap = shpcap
350        GO SUB 1000
360        GO TO 200

600        REM lowpass component is a capacitor
610        INPUT "type normalised lowpass capacitor value (F):";nlpcap
620        LET shpind = (1/nlpcap)*imped/(2*PI*freq)
630        REM now get it printed
640        LET prind = shpind
650        GO SUB 2000
660        GO TO 200

1000       REM capacitor adjusting and print subroutine
1010       IF prcap<1e-9 THEN GO TO 1100
1020       IF prcap<1e-7 THEN GO TO 1200
1030       GO TO 1300
1100       REM value will be printed in pF
1110       LET prcap = prcap*1e12
1120       PRINT "scaled highpass capacitor value = ";prcap;"pF"
1130       RETURN
1200       REM value will be printed in nF
1210       LET prcap = prcap*1e9
1220       PRINT "scaled highpass capacitor value = ";prcap;"nF"
1230       RETURN
1300       REM value will be printed in uF
1310       LET prcap = prcap*1e6
1320       PRINT "scaled highpass capacitor value = ";prcap;"uF"
1330       RETURN

2000       REM inductor adjusting and print subroutine
2010       IF prind<1e-3 THEN GO TO 2100
2020       IF prind<1 THEN GO TO 2200
2030       GO TO 2300
2100       REM value will be printed in uH
2110       LET prind = prind*1e6
2120       PRINT "scaled highpass inductor value = ";prind;"uH"
2130       RETURN
2200       REM value will be printed in mH
2210       LET prind = prind*1e3
2220       PRINT "scaled highpass inductor value = ";prind;"mH"
2230       RETURN
2300       REM value will be printed in H
2310       PRINT "scaled highpass inductor value = ";prind;"H"
2320       RETURN
```

Program 7.6 (LPHPTRAN)

```
5        REM This program is called LPBPTRAN (Spectrum version)

100      INPUT "Type final lower frequency  (Hz):";lfreq
110      INPUT "and final upper frequency  (Hz):";ufreq
120      INPUT "and final impedance (ohm):";imped
130      LET fband = ufreq-lfreq
140      PRINT "Passband bandwidth = ";fband;"Hz"
150      LET fgeom = SQR(lfreq*ufreq)
160      PRINT "Geometric centre fequency = ";fgeom;"Hz"

200      INPUT "Capacitor or inductor (c/l):";c$
210      IF c$ = "l" THEN GO TO 300
220      IF c$ = "c" THEN GO TO 600
230      REM invalid input
240      PRINT "invalid component type, try again"
250      GO TO 200

300      REM lowpass component is an inductor
310      INPUT "type normalised lowpass inductor value (H):";nlpind
320      LET slpind = nlpind*imped/(2*PI*fband)
330      REM now get it printed
340      LET prind = slpind
350      GO SUB 2000

400      REM now calculate bandpass capacitor
410      LET sbpcap = 1/(4*PI↑2*fgeom↑2*slpind)
420      REM now get it printed
430      LET prcap = sbpcap
440      GO SUB 1000
450      PRINT
460      GO TO 200

600      REM lowpass component is a capacitor
610      INPUT "type normalised lowpass capacitor value (F):";nlpcap
620      LET slpcap = nlpcap/(2*PI*fband*imped)
630      REM now get it printed
640      LET prcap = slpcap
650      GO SUB 1000

700      REM now calculate bandpass inductor
710      LET sbpind = 1/(4*PI↑2*fgeom↑2*slpcap)
720      REM now get it printed
730      LET prind = sbpind
740      GO SUB 2000
750      PRINT
760      GO TO 200


1000     REM capacitor adjusting and print subroutine
1010     IF prcap<1e-9 THEN GO TO 1100
1020     IF prcap<1e-7 THEN GO TO 1200
1030     GO TO 1300

1100     REM value will be printed in pF
1110     LET prcap = prcap*1e12
1120     PRINT "   scaled capacitor value = ";prcap;"pF"
1130     RETURN

1200     REM value will be printed in nF
1210     LET prcap = prcap*1e9
1220     PRINT "   scaled capacitor value = ";prcap;"nF"
1230     RETURN
```

continued

```
1300    REM value will be printed in uF
1310    LET prcap = prcap*1e6
1320    PRINT "    scaled capacitor value = ";prcap;"uF"
1330    RETURN


2000    REM inductor adjusting and print subroutine
2010    IF prind<1e-3 THEN GO TO 2100
2020    IF prind<1 THEN GO TO 2200
2030    GO TO 2300

2100    REM value will be printed in uH
2110    LET prind = prind*1e6
2120    PRINT "    scaled inductor value = ";prind;"uH"
2130    RETURN

2200    REM value will be printed in mH
2210    LET prind = prind*1e3
2220    PRINT "    scaled inductor value = ";prind;"mH"
2230    RETURN

2300    REM value will be printed in H
2310    PRINT "    scaled inductor value = ";prind;"H"
2320    RETURN
```

Program 7.7 (LPBTRAN)

```
5       REM This program is called ACTCHEB (Spectrum version)

100     INPUT "Type maximum passband ripple (dB):";ap
110     INPUT "and required order:";nround

200     LET eta = SQR(10↑(ap/10)-1)
210     LET inveta = 1/eta
220     LET a = (LN((inveta)+SQR((inveta↑2)-1)))/nround
230     LET sinha = (EXP(a)-EXP(-a))/2
240     LET cosha = (EXP(a)+EXP(-a))/2

300     FOR k=1 TO (nround+1)/2
310     LET thetak = ((2*k-1)*PI)/(2*nround)
320     LET realpart = -SIN(thetak)*sinha
330     LET imagpart = COS(thetak)*cosha
340     LET w0 = SQR(realpart*realpart+imagpart*imagpart)
350     LET d = -2*realpart/w0

400     PRINT "    d = ";d
410     PRINT "    w0 = ";w0
420     PRINT
430     NEXT k
440     GO TO 100
```

Program 7.8 (ACTCHEB)

passband ripple. Although these designs should be adequate for most applications, it is not difficult to calculate corresponding values for greater orders or different passband ripples[5].

The quantity a is first found from the formula

$$a = \frac{1}{n} \sinh^{-1} \frac{1}{\varepsilon} \tag{7.30}$$

where n is the filter order,
ε is the ripple factor.

A useful formula for determining an inverse hyperbolic sine on a computer which does not have this as a standard function is:

$$\sinh^{-1} x = \ln(x + \sqrt{x^2 + 1}) \tag{7.31}$$

The locations of the poles in the complex plane for the response are given by

$$\alpha_k = -\sin\theta_k \sinh a \tag{7.32}$$

and

$$\beta_k = \cos\theta_k \cosh a \tag{7.33}$$

where $\theta_k = \dfrac{(2k-1)\pi}{2n}$ for $k = 1$ to n $\tag{7.34}$

For even values of n, there will be $n/2$ pairs of poles which are complex conjugates of each other. For odd values of n, there will be one purely real pole (with $d = 2$) and $(n-1)/2$ pairs of complex conjugates poles.

The identities $\sinh a$ and $\cosh a$ are calculated from the relationships

$$\sinh a = \frac{e^a - e^{-a}}{2} \tag{7.35}$$

and

$$\cosh a = \frac{e^a + e^{-a}}{2} \tag{7.36}$$

The complex pole format can be converted into the d, ω_0 format by using equations 7.37 and 7.38.

Programs 7.8 (ACTCHEB) implements these equations, prompting for the passband ripple and the filter order, and printing the values of d and ω_0 for each first and second-order section in the filter.

Root location conversion (program 7.9)

In Chapter 4, it was shown that the response of first and second-order active-filter sections could be described by the values of two variables, d and ω_0. However, many catalogues of active filter designs characterise the responses in terms of α and β, the coefficients of the roots in the complex plane. Equa-

```
5        REM This program is called ROOTS (Spectrum version)

100      INPUT "alpha:";alpha
110      INPUT "beta:";beta

120      LET omega0 = SQR(alpha*alpha+beta*beta)
130      LET d = 2*alpha/omega0

140      PRINT "d = ";d
150      PRINT "omega0 = ";omega0
160      PRINT

170      GO TO 100
```

Program 7.9 (ROOTS)

tions 7.37 and 7.38, originally shown as equations 4.17 and 4.18, convert the α, β format into the d, ω_0 format, and program 7.9 (ROOTS) performs this conversion

$$\omega_0 = \sqrt{\alpha^2 + \beta^2} \tag{7.37}$$

$$d = \frac{-2\alpha}{\omega_o} \tag{7.38}$$

In practice, α always has a negative value, but the program expects a positive value to simplify data entry, and equation 7.38 has been modified appropriately in the program.

Circuit simulation

Throughout this book great emphasis has been placed on the simulation of filter circuits by computer as a way of checking responses before building circuits. As well as being capable of detecting errors in the calculations carried out during design and therefore avoiding the expense of buying the wrong components, simulation also allows experimentation with component values in ways which would be difficult, if not impossible, with real circuits.

Only a few years ago, circuit simulation was a luxury available only to professionals, but all designers, whether professional or amateur, can now obtain programs for many computers, and so can make use of this design tool. Techniques of electronic circuit simulation[6–10] are highly mathematical and generally involve the creation and manipulation of matrices. Rather than trying to explain the technique in detail, this section concentrates on reviewing a commercially available program and giving brief details of other sources of such programs.

The author has tested ANALYSER I, a program available from Number One Systems, Harding Way, Somersham Road, St Ives, Huntingdon, Cambs, for the 48 K Spectrum, BBC, Amstrad and IMB PC (and compatible) computers. A more advanced (and rather more expensive) version with extra facilites, ANALYSER II, is also available for the BBC, Nimbus and IBM machines. The attractiveness of ANALYSER I for the Spectrum is its low cost (£20 + vat) and, despite its rather low speed, freely admitted by its writers, represents extremely good value for money.

Many circuits have been tried on ANALYSER I, and one example is presented here to explain the method of program operation and data entry, though full instructions are provided with the software. Fig. 7.2 shows an active high-pass filter driving a passive low-pass filter, first shown in Fig. 5.26, with each circuit node labelled with a unique (and non-zero) number. When the program is loaded, the main menu is displayed, giving the options shown below

<1>START NEW CIRCUIT
<2>MODIFY CIRCUIT
<3>ANALYSE CIRCUIT
<4>CHANGE ANALYSIS PARAMETER
<5>RE-LOAD CIRCUIT
<6>SAVE CIRCUIT
<7>CHANGE CIRCUIT NAME
<8>CATALOGUE STORE

If option 1 (START NEW CIRCUIT) is selected, the program prompts for a name and the circuit can then be entered. The format of data entry is shown below the circuit diagram in Fig. 7.2: the component designation is entered first, then the node numbers of its terminals, and finally its value. Entry of this data is straightforward, the program prompting for the appropriate data and only accepting correctly formatted inputs. The final entry is a P character, indicating the end of the file, followed by the input, output and

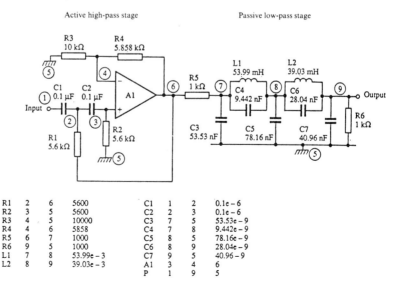

Figure 7.2 *A wideband band-pass filter (first shown in Fig. 5.26) with node numbers added. Below is shown the format of data entry for the circuit*

R1	2	6	5600	C1	1	2	0.1e − 6
R2	3	5	5600	C2	2	3	0.1e − 6
R3	4	5	10000	C3	7	5	53.53e − 9
R4	4	6	5858	C4	7	8	9.442e − 9
R5	6	7	1000	C5	8	5	78.16e − 9
R6	9	5	1000	C6	8	9	28.04e − 9
L1	7	8	53.99e − 3	C7	9	5	40.96 − 9
L2	8	9	39.03e − 3	A1	3	4	6
				P	1	9	5

ground node numbers. As well as the resistors, capacitors, inductors and op-amp shown in this example, the program will handle transistors (bipolar and FET) and transformers.

When the circuit has been entered, the program returns to the main menu and if option 3 (ANALYSE CIRCUIT) is selected, the program will prompt for the number of steps (up to a maximum of 50), the start frequency and the stop frequency. A logarithmic sweep of frequency can be requested by entering a negative number for the number of steps. For this example, the data entered was for 10 logarithmic steps, starting at 100 Hz and ending at 10 kHz. The user is now presented with the sub-menu:

<1> GAIN (dB ABSOLUTE)
<2> GAIN (dB RELATIVE)
<3> GAIN (LINEAR ABSOLUTE)
<4> GAIN (LINEAR RELATIVE)

If the input or output impedance are desired (accessed by choosing option 4 from the main menu) the word GAIN is replaced by Z_{in} or Z_{out} respectively. For this example, we will select option 2 (GAIN dB RELATIVE). An additional prompt, for the relative level, is obtained. Since the circuit has a nominal DC gain of -2 dB, this value was entered. The results for the above example are displayed as:

FREQUENCY	GAIN (dB REL)	PHASE
100 Hz	-18.23	146
166.8 Hz	-9.766	120
278.8 Hz	-3.234	78.4
464.2 Hz	-0.6409	32
774.3 Hz	-0.216	-5.95
1.292 kHz	-0.2045	-43.8
2.154 kHz	-0.2406	-100
3.594 kHz	-2.37	92.5
5.995 kHz	-42.97	150
10 kHz	-41.32	-57.4

If a printer is attached to the computer, a print out of the results can be obtained.

The time taken for an analysis run depends on the number of nodes in the circuit. The Spectrum version of the program is the slowest; on the BBC and Amstrad machines the program runs much faster and is even faster on the IBM PC. The extra memory on the IBM PC also means that circuits with up to 40 nodes and 150 components can be simulated, whereas the limit for the other machines is 16 nodes and 60 components.

Although the example shown was analysed at audio frequencies, ANA-LYSER I is equally capable of assessing the response of RF circuits. A feature of the program which becomes useful at radio frequencies is that it automatically inserts a 0.2 pF capacitor in parallel with each resistor in a circuit, this being a typical value encountered in real components. The capacitor can be removed by entering a capacitor of -0.2 pF in parallel with the resistor.

For such an inexpensive program, ANALYSER I performs well, there being no significant difference in its results and those obtained from a professional package running on a mainframe computer. The speed of operation of the program, even on the Spectrum, is not really restrictive to the amateur, especially when the time taken to design the circuit, enter the data and assess the results, and the potential time and cost penalties of not having a simulator, is taken into account.

Some other sources of circuit simulation programs for use of home computers or cheap IBM PC-type machines are:

1. TRANAP: a listing is available from RSGB Headquarters (see also reference 10).
2. AC LINEAR CIRCUIT ANALYSIS: available from D. Markie, 17, Percy Street, Shepherds Bush, London, W12 9PX. Runs on BBC model B with disk drive.
3. PSPICE: available from Quadrant Communications Ltd, Wickham House, 10 Cleveland Way, London, E1 4TR. Runs on the IBM XT/AT family.
4. MITEYSPICE: available from Pineapple Software, 39 Brownlea Gardens, Seven Kings, Ilford, Essex, IG3 9NL. Runs on the BBC model B (or B + or Master) with 1 disk drive.
5. SPICE*AGE: available from Those Engineers Ltd, 106a Fortune Green Road, West Hampstead, London, NW6 1DS. Runs on IBM XT/AT family.

The prices of programs 3 and 4 probably puts them into the professional league.

Summary and conclusions

The programs presented in this chapter can broadly be divided into three categories:

- those which remove the tedium from filter design by carrying out routine procedures. Programs in this category are ORDER, CSCALE, LSCALE, LPHPTRAN, LPBPTRAN and ROOTS.
- those which allow the designer to produce new designs, not included in the catalogues presented in Chapters 2 and 4. These programs are PASSBUT, PASSCHEB and ACTCHEB.
- circuit simulation packages which allow either existing or new designs to be analysed and assessed for suitability. No program listings were given, but the programs mentioned include ANALYSER, TRANAP, PSPICE, MITEYSPICE and SPICE*AGE.

The programs shown do not represent an exhaustive set for filter design. Using them as typical examples of what can be achieved, others can be written by the reader, for example to convert d, ω_0 values into scaled component values for active filters.

References

1. John Morris, GM4ANB, *Amateur Radio Software*, 1985, RSGB. Appendices: BASIC Program Adaptions, p. 319–24.
2. H.Y-F. Lam, *Analog and Digital Filters: Design and Realisation*, Prentice-Hall. Section 8–1–3, p. 236–8.
3. as reference 2: section 8–2–4, p. 261–2.
4. S. Vickers, *ZX Spectrum* BASIC *Programming*, Sinclair Research Ltd. Chapter 20, p. 111.
5. M.E. Van Valkenburg, *Analog Filter Design*, Rinehart and Winston, 1982, Holt. Section 8.3, p. 233–5.
6. A.S. Beasley, *Circuit Analysis by Small Computer*, February and April, 1980. Wireless World.
7. R.I. Harcourt, *Circuit Modelling by Micro-Computer*, August 1982. Wireless World.
8. P.R. Adby, *Applied Circuit Theory: Matrix and Computer Methods,* 1980, Ellis Horwood Ltd. Chapter 4, Nodal Admittance Matrix Methods.
9. R. Steincross, BASIC *Programming Performs Circuit Analysis,* September 1 1982, EDN, p. 260–1.
10. P.L. Woods, *TRANAP: A Transistor Network Analysis Program,* September 1985, RadComm, p. 698–700. G8HHZ.

Index